NIGHT FREIGHT

ALSO BY CLYDE RICE

A HEAVEN IN THE EYE

NIGHT FREIGHT

CLYDE RICE

BREITENBUSH BOOKS
PORTLAND, OREGON

First Printing:
2 3 4 5 6 7 8 9

Library of Congress Cataloging-in-Publication Data

Rice, Clyde, 1903
  Night freight.

  1. Rice, Clyde, 1903-   2. California—Biography.
3. Oregon—Biography. 4. Gold miners—Pacific States—Biography.
I. Title.
CT275.R532A3 1987   979.5   87-808
ISBN 0-932576-50-8

Breitenbush Books acknowledges the support of the National Endowment for the Arts, a federal agency, for a grant which helped to make the publication of this book possible. The press also wishes to express appreciation to Northwest Writers, Inc. for their support.

Breitenbush Books are published for James Anderson by Breitenbush Publications; Patrick Ames, Editor-in-Chief. General Offices: P.O. Box 02137, Portland, Oregon 97202.

Text design by Patrick Ames.

Manufactured in the U.S.A.

To Virginia Rice,
fifty years my companion,
and to Gary Miranda, superb critic,
and to idealists Jim Anderson and Patrick Ames
of Breitenbush Books,
I give thanks for seeing that this tale
reached you out there—
you, for whom I wrote it.

NIGHT FREIGHT

I WAS JUNGLED UP in some bushes alongside the tracks just outside the railroad yards in Eureka. There was a spring in the bushes and at least twenty bums around smoky fires. Left in my pack was a handful of flour and a small lump of bear fat. I hauled it out and made a twig fire, made it away from the others, feeling I was no bum as they were. Sure, I was going to hop a freight, was broke, but I was no drifter. I was squatting in the rain in a hobo jungle because I'd been out looking for a new way to make a living, taking my chances in the mountains of Northern California. My bundle was big, no ragged parcel, as were most of theirs. I curried my fire while the setting sun found a gap between clouds and horizon and sent its glare through the jungle and against the red boxcars lined behind it.

The smoke of my fire was mingling with mealy smells and the odor of frying. I hunkered over this, hungry as only a man can be who's missed six meals. The thick dough god in the skillet was quite done on one side. I had a fork ready to turn it when the engine at the head of that freight out on the tracks hooted. The bums scrambled their stuff together and rushed through the willows and runt fires to grab a good riding spot.

1

For a second I thought I'd stay and have the bait at ease, but the train hooted again and I stuffed my cooking gear in on top the load, jerked the bindings taut, grabbed it up and parted the willows as the engine's first pull smashed through the freight, setting it slowly rolling. I heaved my pack on the first flatcar that passed and climbed aboard. The flat was loaded with green railroad ties but at the back there was a space about a yard wide across the car somewhat protected from the wind. I had hardly got set on this when an old man hauled himself up on the other side and sat down beside me, then a boy clambered up and over my legs and when we were rolling along starting to gain way, a fourth man came running desperately and made it.

The old man had a full white beard and the last man up had a bottle and on the other side of me, quiet as he shivered, was the long-legged boy with some sort of a kit such as a carpenter or a horse doctor might carry. And, secured to a broken plank in the floor, was my pack with a pick and an axe lashed to the side of it and my thirty-thirty inside.

It was a peculiar way to aim yourself at a goal, just this sitting on the back of a flatcar bound for Frisco; it certainly wasn't the attitude that had brought me clear of the mountains, muling along through seventy-five miles of slush, enduring three sodden camps and last night's washout from the flooded shed in the Indian reservation. The wear of those stumping marches was still more a part of me than my hunger. Now I just sat in the rain being carried along, with the pack that had ridden the spring out of my every stride off my back and beside me, and me with a hand on it as if to commend it for the burdening it had done. It seemed strange paying for transportation with no effort but just endurance, staring up at the sullen dirty red of the following boxcar, listening to the groans and banging of the great iron coupling, the first grip of freight cars, and never unaware of the rolling flanged wheels' indifference as to whether they carried you to heart of family or carved you from existence upon the tracks.

2

I'd been doing some winter prospecting on the second benches of the Pell River, four-days hike away from the railroad. The snow had driven me out of the mountains and I was going home. But I wasn't unhappy, for I'd written half a dozen stanzas of a poem while snowbound under a fir log on the way out. It wasn't much, but it was the best I'd managed in my twenty-nine years and it pleased me.

We were started and we moved about minutely as passengers do to settle down for the trip once it finally starts. We started to make those gestures—at least I did—but I stopped at the absurdity of it and held myself taut inside to take the cold. The rain was hard and steady and the impressive size of my pack was no protection from it in the night. We were four bums on the back of a flatcar of railroad ties banging, grinding down through the canyon of the Eel past winter-gaunted trees and flooding waterfalls along the windings of the swollen river.

We'd been rolling about an hour through the rain when the fellow with the bottle got put to sleep ahead of schedule. He was a wiry guy with a big broken nose and a cauliflower ear and a definite pod below his belt. He had come running through a pelting downpour chased by six or seven vindictive sounding men. "Max," one of them kept bellowing as they came slogging through the puddles, "Max!" That was all. We were rolling at a good rate and the old man had reached over and given him a hand up as he fumbled on the ladder and by the time he sat down beside him, we were out of town and every living thing that could was taking to shelter. We passed several crossings where the lights of waiting automobiles picked us out on our sodden perch and then the freight turned from the warm suburban windows and the distant lights of farms and charged up a canyon as if intent on rooting the river out of it when it gained enough headway.

Max, Jewish from his accent, kept mumbling to himself as he nursed his bottle. The rest of us were silent, aware mostly of the animal heat generated in our centers, building out to be swept from us. The moon had a way of coming out between storm clouds from time to time, lighting the desolate scene before she reeled out of sight and let the rains and the canyon winds have at us again. It was Max who breached the eternal racket of the freight train and started to tell his story. Alcohol, evidently, was a cathartic to his conscience.

"You guys been hanging around Eureka?" His voice was harsh enough to harmonize with the grinding accompaniment. The old man and I held our peace, the kid said it was his hometown.

"Heard plenty 'bout me around town, uh?"

The kid didn't say anything. He looked to be about seventeen or so.

"Ya know me?"

"Uh, uh," the kid answered—it was lost in the racket.

"I bin the fight promoter in Eureka for three years. Ever heard a' Max Dientzer? That wises you, don't it, punk?"

"Well, no," the boy said.

"Skip it," Max sneered. "I get the pitcher. If you ain't hep, you just ain't hep. Yeah," he went on, "they run me outa town—you seen it. Them was Charley Swartz an' Pinch Litoff an' Sammy Dill, and that big guy was Carson E. Glanders. Know 'im, kid? Aw hell, don't tell me. How in hell'd they shake you off the tit, kid—bang you off 'gainst a door jamb?"

"Leave the kid alone," the old man said.

Max got to his feet. I could see him with head lowered at the old man.

"Ya ain't home now, grandpa. That beard's nothin' to me but a handle. Shoot your trap again and I'll soften your bean on them ties."

The old man laughed. There was enough brutal man-force in that laugh to confound a dozen Dientzers. Max took the sound of it into his liver, I'm sure. He shivered, had a bluffing bravado-garnished drink from his bottle, drove the cork home in a punching way, and sat down. He tried a harsh laugh of his own. He could get meanness into it all right but no inference

4

of implacable force.

"Anything to humor ya, grandpa," he muttered and shut up—but not for long. Soon, like upending a garbage can, he was spilling his past before us till we loathed him. He'd been run out, not for doping his fighters or pimping, nor for other matters of double-dealing, but because he'd welched on several bets in the last week.

"The commissioner was the worst, damn him!" he snarled. Then he started to explain his actions as matters of honest greed, the way a cop shows his star to justify certain actions. Max justified himself because he was in it for a fast buck— that was his badge, the crooked dollar.

He stood up and raved it out, his drunken mind trying to rationalize his rottenness, and then for a moment the brandy let him see himself clearly as others saw him and he started screaming. In the dim light I saw him sink his teeth into his arm. He cursed himself in savage monotony and then he tried to jump under the wheels of the following boxcar and the old man reached up and pulled him back down in his place and told him to shut up. He did for awhile.

The old man was big and solid in his rumpled blue suit, and his white beard shone faintly in what reflected moonlight the clouds let through. His dark slouch hat was water-weighted and hid most of his face, but once as we slammed by a deserted station I saw by the light of it his powerful nose jutting out from the black shadows under his Stetson.

Four times he grabbed Max and saved him from the wheels and tried to pacify him. But the fifth time he sat him back with his left hand and then with a short jolt of his right laid him stone cold on the boards and arranged him so he wouldn't fall off.

The rain turned to sleet, then to hail that rattled down on us in the darkness stinging where it struck. Then rain, sleet and hail stopped: there was only the lurching and clanging and the outcast business.

"It ain't that he's fit to live," the old man grumbled, "it's just I'd be seein' his messed-up carcass back there beside the rails—that in my head and this night could be worse than she is."

He kept moving around and in one of those brief moments of moonlight held up the quart brandy bottle, then the light was gone.

"I'll slosh a little where he put his lyin' mouth and then we'll share alike." Then he muttered, "Jesus, it's still half full!"

Any other time you couldn't have got me to touch that pimp-fondled bottle, but when he passed it to me and I spilled some on my lip and it burned before I drank, sheer jubilance soared through me, a heady sense of most of the fumed swallowings of my years. Then I tipped the bottle and gulped three great swallows.

"Here," I said and held the bottle toward the boy beside me. I couldn't see him though he was pressed solidly against me, as was the old man on the other side. There was only room for the four of us as several broken planks at the other side of the boy allowed a big hole where a fifth man could have sat—would have sat, for many bums were on the train and the load of ties at our backs made a species of lee and we could sit flat on the wet deck of the car without our feet hanging over. Even so we were soaking wet, water running down our spines and bellies as we sat leaning against the wet ties.

The boy didn't take the bottle. "Here!" I said. His hand came out in the darkness and fended the bottle back.

"No thanks."

Well, he was just a kid. I'd seen that in the last evening light before we pulled out of Eureka—a pale, gangly young fellow with a sort of preferred innocence about him. His folks, I figured, had made their straight path of righteousness so narrow that it became like tight-rope walking and they could look neither right nor left as they stepped carefully along. Living such a life one was shielded by design as well as by the resulting conditions. I figured that he'd looked most to his ma and pa, at least up until now.

The old man was aware. "Look, Willie," he said with fatherliness in his voice, "we're in for a hard night. Crank down a little of it."

"No," answered the boy. "And my name's not Willie."

The old man chuckled. I could feel it.

"In my book you're Willie," he said. "What *is* your given name?"

"Glen," said the boy.

I belched a most satisfying warm alky-laden belch. Glen, I thought; Mama named him that. Probably because he was conceived in a dandelion-caressed gully behind the house. In the glen. Glen! Never tell anybody the reason, not even Poppa, the lovely Fritz of the first years of marriage. Walk the tight-rope of righteousness still remembering how the blooms of dandelions made the gully a glen and the stiff, waxed points of Fritz's great mustache were rapturous symbols of the piercing.

"Well, Glen," the old man was saying, "you're leaving home for the first time now, ain't ya?"

"Yes, sir. I never been away from Eureka."

"Skippin'?"

"No, I ain't skippin'. I'm going out to make my way."

"First thing you should learn is to take care of yourself, Glen. This windfall apricot brandy'll see us through the night."

"I took the pledge 'fore I left," the boy said.

"Yeah, and now you're starin' right at pneumonia with your innocent blue eyes. That the way Mom wanted it? Sonny, I'm talkin' so much because I'm lookin' out for your Ma's best interests tonight. This slug I'm bent on you takin' is for your own good."

"Yeah," answered the kid, beset with the hand dealt him by the night but still close to home and Mama and Sunday school. "Yeah," he said, "Thanks, but I'll make out without it." I handed the bottle back to the old man and we all kept our thoughts to ourselves for awhile. The bloom of the brandy inside me seemed like a little stove, cherry red with warmth. I didn't notice things for awhile; I actually drowsed. Sleet cut me awake, then moonlight was out. On one side of us I could see the river and on the other the black shadows of cliffs didn't muffle the clattering din of the freight cars nor the cliff's stone-flung echoes. The moon tore past the hole she had found above and I stood up and felt the soreness of my four-day trek galvanized by cold. I stepped over the old man's legs and over the snoring gyp and peered around the corner of the ties. Far ahead on a long curve the locomotive with its stabbing light aimed across the river, rounded a turn and disappeared. I couldn't see a thing after that. I stared out through wind and rain seeing with part of me how the engine had disappeared, while most of me was directed at a face my memory had constructed against the darkness.

He had come to my shack up there in the mountains, had appeared on the trail that came down from the deep snow above me carrying only a carbine—a thirty-thirty, he said later. He greeted me man-to-man and friendly, this Chinaman who the other prospectors down along the trail had warned me about.

"Feed him, sure, but don't turn your back on him," they'd said. "He'll show you a trick with a pan that'll save you days if you can savvy it. He's killed two greenies like you and we know it, but till we prove it he can walk around. Only don't ever take him in for the night or you'll be the third. Just sorta work him to the door after he's et. He'll go, he understands. We all do it, and he won't shoot you through a window. It's somethin' else."

I saw him, the way he looked in my face as he left my door, such a hopping deviltry just beneath the surface and still sad—sad but polite. So strange, and the late dusk blurring it all into hidden agony, and now his face was just like that before me in the dark. What strange life did he lead that he could bed down in some cold bear den and come and eat breakfast with me next morning, so blithely, so jolly about the gold that lay hidden in those hills? As if anyone within the forests of the Pell could ever be truly blithe.

8

Finally our part of the train, our flatcar, rounded the turn and I could see the engine again. They were opening and shutting the fire door as she pounded along and I could see it, and staring the other way I could see the caboose with its light tagging along, riding herd on the train.

"Pretty good size pack you got there," the old man said.

"I got quite a bit of stuff. It's soaked but maybe we could use it."

"Is your carbine rusting?"

"Uh, uh," I answered. "I plugged the barrel with gun grease and gowed the works with it and she's sealed in oil skins. Traded what shells I had for dust before I left." I took my pack from where I had it lashed to the broken decking and started fumbling at the bindings. My hands were swollen, nearly useless, from panning for gold in the icy waters of the Pell. The knots of my load were solidified gnarls.

At a wide place in the canyon we passed a worktrain on the siding. We rattled down past its food smells and its lights and the old man saw I was making no headway with the bindings. "Why'n't you let her go for now," he said. "We've come far enough now to be nearing a water tank. While the engine's taking water and all the bums is moving around, you best have your pack bound and with you. We'll make a fire and warm up."

It made sense to me and I sat down against the old man. "How's the kid?" he said softly. "Weather don't bother me, but I'm some worried about Glen."

"How's Max?" I asked.

"All right," he answered softly, as if he were among sleepers. "I was sitting on two coal sacks but I put them over him while you were standing. Let's put Glen between us." He reached over me and helped the kid while I made space for him. Then we shoved hard against him, and I placed the pack against his legs to shield them from the wind. After about ten minutes, squeezed in against our small warmth, he stopped shaking so uncontrollably. All he said, though, was "No brandy."

"Okay, Willie," the old man said and reached out to feel how Max was doing. Max was awake and in worse shape than the kid. The old man pulled him over to us and gave him a nip from his bottle, feeding it to him as if he were a baby.

"You dirty son of a bitch," Max panted, when he could get his breath. "You slugged me for my bottle."

"Save your steam and keep warm," the old man replied, as he arranged the sodden gunnysacks over Max's legs.

"What's your name?" he asked me.

"Clyde," I answered.

"Married?" he went on.

"Yep," I said, "Married and we have a kid." Pride boiled up in me. "I got a son who's five and a swell wife." I said it too loud I'm sure and I felt him turn to stare, though in that darkness the re-tasting of the seasoning of my words was all he could work with. That, and searching back through the archives of his own emotions.

"That's fine," he said absently, probably thinking of sons of his own. "Kids're top stock," he muttered after a moment.

He said it rather through his nose. It wasn't his view. I figured maybe it had been his father's or his brother's or—*hell!* I told myself, *Lay off it! I'm sick of you sometimes, the way you look for motives and build when you see none. At school you weren't such a godawful "why-er": I don't see the reason you have to put the question to everything now.* But I did.

"Farmer?" I said tentatively.

"Yeah, once," he answered. "Was raised on a farm." He turned to me, "You're not?" Again his question was padded with his surmise. He'd already guessed about a thing before he sought to verify it.

"No," I answered, "though at the moment I'm living on a little place of twenty acres. Got a cow, but it takes more than a cow to make a farmer."

"Yeah," he agreed. "Yeah," and then rather to himself, "takes more than a star to kill the farmer in a man once the seasons have really got him. You, now," he went on hurriedly, "you talk like us and yet you don't talk like us."

"Yeah," I said, "I hear that wherever I go."

"Who digs you meanest about it?" he asked.

"College professors, homburg-hatted salesmen."

"You get around."

"Not much," I answered.

"You're no honest-to-god miner. I know that. What's the tumble?"

"Oh, I prospect and pan and sluice but I'm no miner," I answered. "It isn't my trade. Tell you—I'm a jack-of-all-avocations. My only qualifying mark is not being a journeyman at anything."

Again I felt his turning, his regard in the darkness, turning not to see me but to focus all of himself on me. "It's what I figured," he said. "Crafts leave a great callous or a warped gait."

"Sure," I agreed, "but did you ever walk along feeling your purse floating around in your back pocket like an empty Durham sack? Did you ever walk along hating the clasp on the purse as it held away securely on nothing?"

"It skipped me," he said, "but I see what you mean and I envy you your knowing."

That kind of thinking didn't fit a farmer.

"What were you," I asked, "I mean in your prime?"

The moon spun from the stampeding clouds and we saw each other as visible entities. The old man's face was completely hidden in shadow, his head bent forward into his beard as if his sagacity were centered there, as if he were asking promptings from his symbol of seniority. As I stared, the train carried us through a thick grove of evergreens. His voice was close by my ear in the blackness.

"In my prime I was a farmer and a sheriff, and I sheriffed and farmed till my sons were in their prime."

"Which craft marked you?"

"Crafts weren't the thing that done it," he answered. "I

never felt the overalls or the badge become part of me but I build two solid fronts in my time. Trouble was, neither was squarely mine."

"Sure," I laughed, "and that's why you can surmise on me."

He chuckled—a little weakly, I felt. "That's about the size of it," he answered.

We said all this leaning heavily against Glen with Max pulled up against the old man and plastered with the wet sacks. The wind had left the canyon but in the sky I saw it had blown the clouds away. Far ahead the engine whistled.

"COMIN' TO THAT WATERTANK," the old man said, "Let's keep together. Stay with us, Glen, and you best stick too," he said, shaking Max's shoulder. "Soused as you are you'd be rolled 'fore you could walk four car-lengths from the fire."

"Wait'll I spill who got the bottle," muttered Max.

"You won't and we both know it. You're hep to things. Another thing," he said to all of us, "let's get back here 'fore she starts pulling out. There's worse perches on this train and we'll find it out if we're late."

When she battered to a stop we got off on the bank side. "Hell," the old man said, "it ain't gonna be on this side," and then we climbed back to the other side. I saw other bums heading for the middle of the train. When we got there a little guy had stolen the oily, thready waste that's jammed into the wheel bearings and, holding the oily mass before him like Perseus with the Gorgon's head, flung it against the wall of rocks and set it afire. In the dark others groped up branches and trash along the high water mark of the river and soon had set them aflame. In five minutes we stood in a half circle around the lusty bonfire.

Soaked through, chilled to the center of their innards, men jostled around until a caste system was effected. The weak, the halt, and the puny were pushed back to the outer perimeter.

Two small Irish thugs dressed in double-breasted dark suits that didn't hide the guns in their shoulder holsters stood to the flames, legs wide apart and caps dragged low. They looked each of us up and down and one of them snarled from the corners of his mouth, "She breaks off at Chi! She just breaks off! Even the dicks out here is diffrunt." I figured they were on the lam until things cooled off a little bit in the east.

Steam rose from us. We were in a strange ferment in which gracious moves were made by hardened men once they had established themselves in the place allowed them between the outer boundary of dark and cold and the inner boundary of fire itself. They bucked and cussed and threatened and, when they could, twisted sideways to allow some heat to flare out to the weak. I noticed such gestures in three or four.

There must have been thirty of us around that fire and how good the heat was! Several of the weaker ones on the outskirts said they planned to stay the night by its warmth and catch another train, and while they bided their time the rest of us soaked the heat up and dreaded the wet and cold of our transportation.

"Five more minutes," yelled a soft-hearted brakeman from the train.

"Ah let 'em rot!" bellowed another from farther up the tracks.

Some cursed the latter brakeman, none commended the first.

We turned ourselves this way and that before the fire, each man holding his belongings tightly to him. The steam that rose from us was borne away by a draft that came creeping out of some gully in the canyon wall. It brought back the feel of Muletail Basin up the Pell, where drafts snaked through the silent forest with a stealth and fearsomeness that set a loner's backhair up. I turned and watched Max struggling with the forces set against each other in him. He hated the old man for clouting him and for taking his bottle, and he'd heard him

14

admit to being an ex-cop. Still, Max probably had a wad of bills on him and maybe he figured the old man suspected a Jew would never leave a town empty-handed. Maybe the old man would squawk if he squawked. Seeing him drunk without the old man siding him, they might roll him. The set of his mouth was full of knowledge and complaint but he didn't spit any of it out. He just soaked up what heat he could and bit tight on his gall of knowledge.

We made another turn before the flames and then the kid helped me on with my pack and we started back to our windbreak of ties. But Max tripped and fell in a hole full of bramble of evergreen blackberry, and before we got him out and on his feet many had passed us in the rush for sheltered riding spots.

When we got to our car of ties our place was taken, jammed somehow with six men who sat stout and silent. When Max started shouting at them the old man slapped him on the mouth and dragged him along and maneuvered us to the forward end of the car, where we clambered up on top of the ties. He had hardly followed us up to our new place when, with a tremendous jerk that rattled through the string from engine to caboose, we started rolling downgrade and fast.

The old man was almost spilled from the ties, but the kid caught him and grabbed his hat and handed it to him. For a moment he lost command: he was a toppled, bemused ancient. Time and its frailty can't be wholly hidden. It shows and strikes in the unguarded moments, and in that moment I saw the snowy beard as the white flag of frailty, of brittleness. A sorrow at the mortality of all of us seeped through me somewhere, and then the old man slowly righted himself from his thrown position, jammed his hat on the bulbous cranium that topped his lean temples and, sitting, up, took chiefhood and cognizance of our position.

"Git your backs to the wind and sit on your coattails." he squalled.

I was sorry for him; I'm sure Glen was too. We complied quickly and felt the wind begin to tear all memories of the fire from our bodies.

We sat lumped together on the wet ties. Ahead of us a boxcar much higher than our stack of ties should have broken some of the wind but didn't. After much fuss and improvisation the old man sat facing backward and blocked the wind with his broad back. I sat my big pack against his back and tied the shoulder straps about him. Next, Glen gave up his coat to protect the old man's head and shoulders, then sat facing backwards, his uncoated back against the old man's belly. He sat within the old man's spread legs. I sat in a like manner against the boy, as did Max against me. Jammed together this way we presented my pack and the old man's head and shoulders to the streaming wind. The long freight bored on through the biting cold of the canyon while atop the ties we presented the edge of our bizarre shape to the elements. We were doing all right. I had a moment to think of the sweetness and warmth I was heading toward. I even slumbered for a moment dreaming of her and awoke with a start realizing the breath on the back of my neck wasn't my wife Nordi's but the kid's. He was slumped against me in a momentary doze.

"What are you thinking of right now?" I asked over my shoulder.

"Shoes," he replied at once, though ruminatively, "handmade shoes. What were you thinking of?"

I dodged it. Even my wife's name was too warm, too personal, to air in this canyon. I started to say I was thinking of how good kitchen smells are in the winter, but didn't. Hell, that would have made him homesick. "I was thinking of the steam off a bowl of beans," I said.

"How's Max doin'?" the old man broke in on us.

Max said, "Honk the old bastard," and burrowed harder against my cooling gut.

I was thinking again of Nordi and the sturdy way that my boy Bunky walked, almost manly at five, when I felt the kid

16

swivel his head around, so I looked around too. A continuous mass of black cloud had taken half the sky and sped as we stared, its ugly curtain smothering it all.

"It's a full gale up there," the old man said. "Glad we're down here in this canyon."

Then sleet hit us and some of the bottom side of that high-flung gale. There was rain in the sleet that plastered and froze—not a lot of it, but it was steady. It began building a glaze on everything, even our eyeballs, and the bums on the train began to move about in spite of the glassy danger. They started shifting, looking for better lees, better hide-outs. They began creeping around us, moving to keep from freezing rigid in the dark. In all of us, I think, was a mutual bitterness: we who varied, we who in our aimless searchings faced the cold, the mob, our countless failings; we who secretly treasured that maleness that made us stray, hated it now as the sleet ripped down to anchor or to drive us.

A small guy came over the top of the ties dragging with him his brief bundle. He tried to find a lee at the side of us. "We'll freeze sure as hell," he yelled as he hunkered against us. He scrambled around and finally crawled up to look up at the boxcar ahead. Then he worked back. "They's a little trapdoor high up on the end, but it's sealed." He crouched, pressed against us in the gale. Ice built on our faces, but we were still loathe to leave our position, for we kept some brief memories of warmth in our backs and bellies. My feet were freezing through and my hands number than the Pell ever made them. Finally, staying put any longer just didn't make sense.

Max scrambled off and I got on hands and knees and crawled along the glaze and stood up and swung out from the post that held the carload of ties from slipping. It was rough but I finally reached myself up and out and got a foot against that swaying boxcar ahead and cut the aluminum tape of the seal with my knife. Then the old man was there helping, steadying me as the jerking cars worked to shake me loose. Not a word was spoken. Between the cars the racket of the grinding wheels and the slam of couplings drowned all other sensation. I swung across and shoved the little door wide and got an arm and then half my body through. I felt the old man pushing my feet and then I was in where it was still and warm, lying on dry lumber a foot or so below the door. I reached out for him and heard him yell, "Here's your pack!" He passed it and I worried it through the door. Next he passed me Glen, and then Max and the little guy who had crawled to our lee, and then he swung his big old body across that loud canyon. As I anchored myself and helped him in, I felt his ice-laden beard drag over my ear and then he was in and other black silhouettes came scrambling across the glazed ties and chanced the iced foot places and trusted our hands as they came through. There must have been a dozen of us lying in the dry before the old man closed the door.

"Any of the train crew see it open and we'll all be in the clink," the old man said.

"Warm clink," a voice near me said softly.

Somebody lit a match, another guy had a flashlight beam playing around the place. Most of the car was loaded to the roof with planed lumber, but there were spaces in it where a group of shorter lengths left a place a fellow could crawl into, for we were all packed awkwardly and rigidly in the space by the door. From within the car the storm seemed distant and the rumble of the wheels less implacable. All round me I heard rubbings and chafings as each man sought to bring circulation back to icy hands and neck and cheeks. I wanted a nip out of the old man's bottle, as I'll wager did Max and the old man, but it was out of the question in here. Still it was a glowing thing to know we had it.

Glen wriggled down into one of the pockets in the lumber and found a small place for himself and his brassbound kit. Max moved over until he was against the side of the car. By then the guy with the flashlight had turned it off. Wind and sleet and the bulk of the freight train's racket were walled away. The outgoing heat of our breathing began to warm the place; there was even some vestige of warmth from the lumber.

"They musta piled it in here from right outa the kiln," a guy said from the corner. "Even smells kind of burnt."

"Kiln dryin' should take a week," another voice said. "In Arkansas we give red oak two weeks."

"Yeah," answered another, "but they're speeding it up, buddy. I got a couple of days work in the redwood kiln in one of them towns up there and the guys admit they're just toasting it. They know it makes it brittle and near useless, but any top guy in a plant now has got to be a quick turnover man or he ends up walking down the street talking to himself."

"Anyway," another bum was saying to a couple of guys jammed against him, "there's plenty wood in the Eureka country to cook up a little chow once you scrounge the makings. Say you're mooching in Frisco or L.A. They ain't any money, but say some old Gert falls for your pitch and ponies up an egg or two. By Jesus, you spend the rest of the night cornering all the burnt matches in three city blocks to cook it with."

"Don't you know how to suck eggs?"

"No, and I ain't gonna try. They ain't much suck in me anyway. I'm a bum, sure, but I'm still a doggoned good man."

"Why ain't you working?"

"I told you—no suck."

"Yeah," said a sad voice far ahead from a hole in the lumber, "but neither knuckling or suck helps much now."

"It's because this civilization is decadent as hell, rotten as crap," enunciated an eager voice. Nobody answered and into the silence the fellow interjected more of his line. "We're class-ridden and just like Marx says classes is gotta go."

"Marx?" someone asked? "Where's he?"

"He's been dead about fifty years," someone answered him.

I snickered. "So are Anthony Comstock and Mary Baker Eddy," I said.

The old man gave me a dig in the ribs.

"Marx says classes is gotta go," the zealot went on, "and they've done away with them in Roosia. Right now everyone's free and equal and owning the tools of production in Roosia. In a state like that, there just can't be any tyranny. Everybody'll be living like kings in a coupla years. There's no waste in Roosia and you know how much waste there is in a capitalistic society. Our leaders ain't not only got to have the best but they throw it away half-used."

"Makes for longer snipes," ruminated a voice near me in the darkness.

"Why, the Czar had hundreds of political prisoners in Siberia. That's the way capitalistic regimes handle fellows that think for themselves. But the communists sure put a stop to that, they just opened them barred doors and they love the nigger and the Jew. Everybody's just a worker there whatever, and a worker gets a month a year to go sit in the Crimea and eat oranges."

"Hell," said a squeaky voice near me, "Roosevelt's got this country back on its feet and going again. It's gonna get better, and most folks got nothin' against Jews or niggers, 'cept to be ashamed for the way us others has treated them."

"Seein' the whole world through dialectic materialism," the propagandist continued, "you can understand pret' near everything and what can't be explained by that system must be lies the bosses has cooked up. Take like property. It seems natural for a guy to pile it up for a rainy day and we got to believing it is natural, but it ain't. They let on like that in print 'cuz they want you to buy a new blanket or shoes, but if you do you're just being the stooge for capitalists."

"Aw, break it off, will ya?" complained a voice. "Can't a bunch of 'boes get together in a boxcar or a jungle without some earnest John trying to make a communist or a Christian out of you?"

Another guy snorted. "If I knew of a class of people," he said, "that wasn't lousy with these anxious-earnest bastards, I'd try to jine it even if I had to work."

20

The train went over a bridge and we all listened to the hollowness below us. After we were across everyone was quiet for a moment. The old man broke into it. "Listen," he said, "we're slowing up to a stop. We ain't to Willow Point, yet we're stoppin' and if we're not damn quiet in here they'll notice that the door ain't got no seal."

When the jarring stop came we were silent. There was just the dark and the easy breathing of men. I lay listening to the many variations in breathing, figuring that it came from many things—character, shape of nose, the amount of hair in it. I even got to considering the various strengths of diaphragms that pushed it. I'd made quite a summation of the various processes attendant to breathing, when the drivel-pusher started whispering loudly about the tools of vested interests.

I began to feel sorry for him. In my book propagandists fall mainly in two categories—those who know how simplified and inaccurate a program of action must be to appeal to the mutts the program is supposed to be for, and then the worse kind, the ones that eat their own propaganda.

The communist went on in his hoarse whisper using that lingo of theirs, punctuated the way Christian Science is with those special words. Once-removed polysyllables seem the basic need of these two extremes of concept, while down the middle we got along somehow, resting on humor and some scepticism and an overall acceptance of life and letting the others—the ones who wanted to ram it into a sock, tie a string around it and call it theirs—howl at the moon.

The trainman came within several cars of us and opened a coupling and broke the compressed air brakeline and the forward part of the train went on up the tracks and we lay and listened to it go and we all guessed, I suppose, about some cars standing on a siding full of lumber in the dark and how the engine and part of the train would hook up to them and how and why they would be cut into the center of the train. We could no longer hear the engine. The brakeman and his companion came closer to us until they were standing beside our car. The other fellow evidently had once been a brakeman on this line too, though now he had a job out there somewhere in the brush with the mill that was shipping those cars of lumber.

They talked along about the little things they'd known together. "Oscar still living on powdered alfalfa?"

"Hell yes," the brakeman answered, "and still wearing cantilever shoes and brings his own bottled water for the iron in it, he says."

The mill man chuckled, "Still carry that spud in his pocket to absorb aches and pains?"

"Yep."

One of the men started kicking at the gravel. We could hear it when a piece would knock loose and fly out into the brush.

"Gladys still waitin' table at the Owl?"

"Of course! Wouldn't be the Owl without her."

"She sure ain't young as she used to be."

"That's right," the brakeman said solemnly. "Never was. Jesus, it's cold!"

"A rotten night," agreed the millman. "The highway's closed between here and Garberville," he went on. "Full of blow-down hemlocks and firs. Them redwoods always stay put."

"Maybe," answered the brakeman. "By God we come through a lot of wind and sleet while back. Most of the bums left at the watertank, rest's hid somewhere in a boxcar. Busted a seal I figger."

"You gonna get the crew together and pry 'em out?"

"I should a' course, but I ain't. That sleet back there was more than a man's built to stand. It cut through the canyon for better'n an hour. No sir, if they're holed up and safe I'm plain relieved. Fact, in the winter the misery of the bums gets me down. I'm only sixth from the bottom of the seniority list now. Well, here she comes."

After they had banged the whole line of cars around for awhile and hooted and tooted like it was mating time for locomotives we got under way again. A fellow in the car said,

"I don't know what there is about this cold on the coast—wet cold just don't cover it. Being wet couldn't get it at your bones the way this does. I'm from North Dakota and I've seen some god-awful weather but never nothin' like the cold in here along the Eel River when she gets sleety."

Other fellows chimed in. Each guy had to speak of the spectacularness of the weather in his particular community and then everybody was quiet, listening to a flat wheel and time and memories. Then a fellow behind me started telling another guy, who had lost his farm, about his dame trouble.

I was beginning to feel comfortable at last. Gradually warmth drove away all coldness from my bones and a feeling of the luxury of living came over me. I shoved my feet against my pack and leaned back and found there was space enough to lie flat on the lumber with my knees up and the toes of my shoes dug under the pack. After a moment that luxuriant feeling came strong again and the words "creature comfort" popped into my mind. I wanted to laugh. I was thinking that most of the labels have been pasted cockeyed on the things they are supposed to define. We rocked over a section of track poorly laid and I rolled elegantly with each lurch. It was good, like the satisfaction old folks must get out of their rocking chairs.

The guy with dame trouble was well into his third woman by now, and the farmer was so wound up in the erotic details that, when the guy fumbled in his story and left an opening, he didn't interject his own tale of spavined horses and hard water. He just waited as the guy went on telling how they didn't come in front of the keyhole for quite awhile but when they did—and so on. I listened for awhile myself, hungry for thinking on women after my sojourn from them in the mountains. Then his talk dwindled in my ears. I lay seeing panoramically, but intimately too, all the country I'd passed through on my trek to the railroad. What is it, I wondered, that makes a guy like me go prospecting in the winter? Sure, the Robbling job was closed down and would be for a month and a half, but what drove me to make elaborate preparations with the few hard-earned dollars of my savings? Wasn't any use saying I did it for money. I was beginning to realize I went on these journeys for a lot of reasons and that none of them ever got clear to the front of my mind. One of those shadows I only half-faced, making up the bulk of the real me, was the need for solitude and distance to give focus to my views. Maybe the trek was in way of being a ritual. It must be, to maintain meaning while being so illogical, and yet so satisfying to my innermost self.

Then my almost-dreaming shot back and I was remembering a thick bunch of scrub redwoods I had come upon in the evening my first day in from Eureka. It had been over two months ago. There was wind and rain then too, and the scrub looked like a perfect windbreak. I wanted to make my camp and spend the night there. Instead, I plugged along past it wrapped up and sightless. I spent a rotten night several miles further on, in rolling high meadow country, my little tent blown down three times by the gale.

All the way in to where the Pell joins the south fork of the Siskiyou I trudged along, staring at the grandeur of the mountains and the poetry of the changing sky, and all I thought or really saw was the Robbling's Dock and the doings on the dock. Most clearly I saw Jed, the steelworker, his mouth full of sandwich just bitten off and the sandwich in his hand as yet not lowered from in front of his face. I would see his eyes glare as he received some barbed remark of mine and then I would watch how he'd shift his quid of sandwich to his cheek, make his hot rejoinder, follow it with an obscenity at me, and then start chewing, glaring at me and sizing up the sandwich for the next bite while the other fellows stared at the floor as they chewed because of the fury of their views. How clearly I felt the lunchroom benches and the air of lunchtime with the smell of fresh paint, of fried chicken and wood shavings, of coffee and the stale rancid smell of the tallow on the leather belts of a machine they kept there. I felt most intimately all that fussing with thermos bottles and thermos tops and waxed paper and napkins as I went walking along. I, who for months had longed only to get away from the grind of the dock and my relations with the crew; I, who talked and dreamed of mountains eternally, couldn't see them when they were before me. "Hell, I live fore and aft, never man enough to come to grips with now," I muttered—soundlessly, I thought, but again the old man dug me in the ribs.

"Them that's only good at now," he mumbled, "is a sad horse for anything but standing still."

Max was telling somebody who he was and the why of it with the overtones of injured dignity.

"You should have left him to the big dealers back there in the yards," I grumbled. I felt cheap as soon as it was uttered.

"I don't know," the old man answered. "It paid off a snort apiece and a little more stored by. Anyway," he went on, lowering his voice, "I figger that whatever a guy's done he's got a right to get out of town. I'm not countin' perversion crimes, I'm talking about man stuff. Murder and rape ain't so heinous, they're just extremes called up by instinct. If a man owns a towering feeling for his country, say, he'll be topply with his other feelings too, and thievin's more natural than honesty. Just watch any animal. I don't know about bugs and bees, but I notice that all us spined ones's got an instinct for it and I've noticed too it isn't the strong folks that deny a lenient view, it's the timid unsparked ones that's always putting more barbed teeth in the law. A man with any more crust to him than milk toast will be hard put to stay out of their jails in another ten, twenty year."

I snorted agreement then heard a voice behind me that by its general sound and intonations build a picture inside me of its owner: small, sturdy, loyal, neat on the job and dextrous, but not built to inspire bosses or women. I knew the kind. I had an uncle like that once. He was meek at night and did calisthenics each morning. This fellow behind me was a seaman of sorts.

"Ya know," he was saying, "rocking along on the top of this boxcar reminds me of the *Fairweather.*"

"So what?" said his companion.

"The old *Fairweather* was a fishing tug I was a hand on in 1927." He waited. Nobody said anything. I was sure he was quite eager to yarn but somebody had to ask, just like Uncle Delbert. Nobody said anything. They knew him in the dark as I did, and weren't going to give him a break. They weren't the kind, so I did.

"Was that down in Frisco?" I asked.

"God, no," he answered gratefully. "Ya see," he said, "the tug's named after this mountain up there—Alaska, that is. Mt. Fairweather is 15,399 feet high. I looked it up, working on the boat and all. We towed stuff around up there and brailed the traps. That's all salmon up there, you know—chums and kings and humpies. We'd fill our hold and then load a couple of barges afore we brailed all our traps—we had seven. The *Annie* had nine, but then—"

"To hell with the *Annie!*" someone said. The seaman quit his tale feeling hurt, and at once we forgot about the *Fairweather.*

The boxcar strained as we swung around a sharp turn, the steel wheels ground against the steel rail and between them they made a long, shrill scream, then we lurched the other way and onto a straightaway where the cars rolled easily.

"Never been to Alaska," the old man mused, though to me too. "That's what comes when you let home and work sap the wild Harry outta you."

I wasn't itching to get away from home, and so at the moment I couldn't accept his view. Home was a light in the dark that got bigger as you trudged closer. And you didn't knock, you called out before you got to the door and those that had been waiting while you'd been gone opened it and the light streamed out, and the warmth and their voices and the smell of cooking. Right then I'd've traded all the wild Harrys that had ever been in me to be able to be stepping the last half mile over the ridge taking the cutacross, the bay spread out darkly with its outer fringe of dimly lit towns, and down below me in the little valley a tiny light from a window.

Seemed like everybody was through with talk at least for awhile. God knows how many memories and hungers, how much stifled revenge and going-away selfless love, could have been found in the hearts of those who rode that boxcar. I fell asleep, though I was never unaware that I slept jammed against strangers—that is, until I was dreaming.

It was one of those sex dreams a fellow gets. My wife gets them, and I once ran around with a girl who dreamed them every night. Anyway, there's this heightened awareness, the ecstatic new perception of something taken for granted before, that finally reaches a blissful stage impossible to communicate. I dreamed of a cow once who, when I patted her flank, swung her well-proportioned Jersey head around and gave me a look of such warm, amorous regard, that it still seems I was once married to her.

Now as I lay with the bums I dreamed of the wife of an acquaintance of mine. Saunders was his name, an odd character who visited us often with wife and dog. She was a rather colorless little woman who was always chasing her Daschund pet that wasn't quite housebroken and wouldn't stay at her side. "Now, Queenie, Queenie," she would scream all the time they were visiting, "Queenie, come here!"

Her husband and I fancied ourselves fine shots and when we weren't hunting we would sit in the kitchen, Nordi busy with the paraphernalia of a coffee klatch. It would be steamy and the smell of baking bread would be in our nostrils as we talked of trajectories and windage, and we took gulps of coffee and small bites of coffeecake so we'd be ready to break into the other fellow's tale of how well he'd done, with our own tale as boastfully inaccurate as his. It was a species of bravado that we put up with in the other fellow so we might in turn roll some of it over our tongue with the liar's largesse. The trouble was I'd worked for about five years with Saunders, rode to and from work with him and, though we weren't close, the companionship of proximity had made us like brothers. I knew of every shot he'd ever taken, knew all of his better lies and couldn't forget some of the worst and he knew it, so really I can't see why he visited us for a rehashing and re-rehashing of how he downed a duck. And all the time we'd boast of our prowess his mousy woman with her reedy voice would be screaming, "Queenie, Queenie, now Queenie!" as the dog tried to get set to piddle in the kitchen or the room adjacent.

As a female, Mrs. Saunders had never existed for me, and now on the swaying, grinding freight I dreamed of her. She lay on the ground next to our house, stretched out tight against the wall of it as if she had fallen in a faint and was immobilized. Her grey eyes stared up steadily into mine. All about her were the tall stocks of hollyhocks, for she lay in a broad flower garden bordering the house and under her and about her was a flat plant with small, hairy leaves and little flowers of coarse odor. I pushed through the hollyhocks and knelt by her head and she moved until she could rub her cheek against my trousers at the knee, then she was still. Her mousy hair, almost grey in its neutralness, bore sly, shy richness in its sheen. I looked down into a face slender, yet with Slavic strength in the cheekbones, and touched her eyebrows. They were of a soft neutralness—like mouse fur, I thought, but long. I caressed them following their curve carefully. They grew damp under my touch and her eyelids became dewy, like petals in the morning. I raised her arms and placed them carefully around her head and the wide-sleeved dress fell away and revealed her armpits where that strange soft hair grew luxuriantly. I caressed the delicate rhythms of it and it too became erotically humid. Then I awoke and lay wondering why I had never seen such subtleties in Saunders' wife.

The train swayed and racketed along as I drowsed. It was becoming quite stuffy with all us unwashed ones jammed together, the small space becoming vapor-laden from our breathing.

A fellow down in one of the pockets in the lumber forward was mumbling to a man lying on top the load there and soon several were talking around him. Then we were all aware.

"I tell ya, it's moving," the man up forward shouted. "This guy's down here and can't get out. It's worked a board over him while he was sleepin' and he says another one's starting to push at him."

The true hobo who had been making remarks about Depression bums versus professional hoboes spoke up smugly: "Never catch an honest-to-God 'bo getting in a hole in lumber. Lumber works sometimes to a swayin' boxcar. More'n one guy has had a two-by-four shoved through his guts and nobody ever wise till they unloaded the car or smelled him. How you other guys down in the holes?"

The fellow with the flashlight had it on and searched the hollows in the lumber. By its light I saw that Glen had a large board between him and freedom, and that there was another guy even deeper down and in worse trouble. As we stared we could see some of the pieces moving—microscopically, but moving. The men up forward reached down into the shallow hole where their trapped man was and, all grasping the restraining board, tried to break it off. Failing that, they tried to force it back the way it came. In the meantime the old man had slipped my small axe from its bindings and passed it forward. They soon chopped the board in two and got their man out.

Glen and the other man were in deep, narrow holes. I tried to get down in the hole where Glen was and chop the plank that all but filled his route of escape, but the axe handle was too long and in that narrow place it just wouldn't work. The old man had the rope off my pack by then. It was half-inch line, much too big for its job, but handy now. We doubled it and wrapped it around the plank and pulled. But from the prone positions we had to take we couldn't get our backs in it and were unable to budge the plank. Then the hobo jammed the handle of my axe in the crack in the lumber and forced carefully until the handle broke, leaving only room for your two hands. The little guy who had crawled in our lee out on the ties wiggled down by Glen and pecked and chopped until he weakened the plank so that we could break it with the rope. Glen crawled up hanging onto his box.

"Thanks," he said with a disbelieving air, as if he wasn't certain all this had happened to him since he left that warm kitchen some few hours past.

The last man was locked down deep, five different boards blocking his way out.

"We got to pile the lumber off him," the little guy with my axe said. "There's more stuff working to push through."

"We can pile it forward," the old man said.

He got the seaman to go forward to store the lumber as tight as he could and then he started shifting it. I got two candles out of my pack and lit them in their coffee tin reflectors so we could save the flashlight. We had very little room to work in and too many men in what space there was. We got three planks removed from the hole and then it became difficult as we dug deeper into the pile. We were able to break many of the longer pieces where we could get leverage, but the whole load was interwoven as to board length and our lumber-moving was onerous. We couldn't seem to get the fourth board loose, and the boards were now stacked so tightly in the car that five or six fellows climbed out and rode the tie car to make more room. Still we couldn't budge it. We tried moving more lumber but were unable to and we found that in moving we'd buried my axe under the lumber pile.

"Come on," the fellow under the board groaned, "get me outta here. It's moving by my head!" He had been cutting the board with his knife. Then Glen got a hooked knife out of his kit and got down and whittled stubbornly on the top of the board. When he slowed down in his whittling, the professional bum lifted him out and got down and finished the job with a wicked-looking blade and then, prying up the ends, we broke them and set the trapped man free. The man crawled out saying nothing, then crawled out through the little trapdoor and crouched on the ties, they said afterward, until the train hit a steep grade and slowed. He got down on the boarding ladder then and, heaving his bundle into a bush, jumped off and made it. Hope he got a fire going somewhere.

THE TRACKS AND WHEELS hit up a wild rhythm after we topped a rise and soon we were rolling at a great rate, but the lumber we'd piled around in the rescue was on the move around us so that we began to fear it and anyhow the professional bum told so many lumbercar horrors that we were glad to get shut of it when the old man said that, considering the broken seal and all, we'd better get out.

At Alder Point most of the bums left the train figuring to go down the track a ways and build a big fire so they could dry out before they holed up in a barn the true hobo had spotted.

"How about you?" the old man asked. "You gonna knuckle to the weather?"

"No," I answered, "once I get going in a direction, the going just takes over. I don't think I could hole up now even if I wanted to."

"Probably because you're going toward a woman," he muttered bleakly.

"Well, yes and no," I answered. "Works as good when I'm going away from her 'cept that she's there, and real."

"Makes no difference," he answered. "I know about the other."

"Your wife," I asked, "she alive?"

"Dead," he answered after a moment of thoughtful stillness. "Nine years."

I murmured that I was sorry, feeling cheap for my prying.

"So am I," he said, "so am I." Then he forced himself from the past and looked about him. "Where's Glen?" he asked, grabbing manfully at the present.

Glen was sitting on his box almost under our feet in the deep shadows of the station. "Right here," he said.

"Are you gonna stay here for the night or go on?" the old man asked.

"I'll keep going," Glen answered, "Pop said not to tarry by the way."

I had a brief vision of their home, the walls of its clean rooms cluttered with framed, decorated mottoes. I could see the room so clearly that I could even see the pictures of Glen's grandparents taken in the old country. The grandmother appeared to be consumptive and frightened while grandpa's fierce mustaches were matched by his eyes for sharpness. He was in military uniform and stood poised to defend country and honor.

Then I did one of those thoughtless, impelled things: "What did your grandfather on your father's side do in his military service?" I asked Glen.

"Why, he played the flute in the band," Glen answered. "Gosh!" he said and then smiled. "Why?"

"I don't know," I answered. "Just one of those things."

The old man came closer to me and as we stood in the dim lights around the station I saw him peering at me. "By God, you're a strange one," he said, and then he shifted his thoughts. "What we've got to do is find a better spot to ride."

"Why'n't you stay here for the night?" I asked him.

"Could," he said, "I easy could. Still, following the will-o'-the-wisp is a tangled business. Seems you can dally all you want in your ease, but stop in the rough spots—why, it's hanging through the rough spots that keeps your dues paid in this union. No, what we got to do is find a better spot and now is the time to look for it. Where's Max?"

"In the station by the stove," Glen said.

We found him with a crowd of footloose characters around the station stove. The clock on the station wall said eleven-thirty more or less. I went over to Max and asked him to come outside.

"Sure," he said. "Ya know, I like you. You ain't afraid to bust in a car if that's what you want to do. You and me could get along fine."

He followed me out to the old man. "Give me my bottle," he said as soon as he saw him.

"Uh, uh," the old man grunted. "I stalled you from jumping a couple of times tonight and you're paying in brandy, even having a nip of it from time to time yourself. Look, Max, you gonna hole up here tonight?"

"Nah," he answered and stood for a moment reeling solemnly in front of us. "Got no use for this whole redwood country. I'm going straight through Frisco and then down to L.A."

"Come on then," the old man said, "we're gonna find a better place to ride."

"Gimme a drink?"

"I'll do that when we're out of town. Now come on!"

We poked along the freight in the dark, our only light being from the station and town. Our luck was dim as well. All the tie cars were worse than the one we'd been on and it was still raining. Then I found a car of ties with a hollow space in the center that opened clear across the car. We wouldn't be able to sit upright in it, but there was plenty of leg room and we'd be sheltered from the wind and rain. I climbed up and felt around and found why the ties had been piled around it. In the decking of the car was a big hole: over a third of the decking was gone. I showed it to the old man.

"Look here," he said almost at once, "here's our chance. Now you three scrounge around for boards to cover it and shove what you get up in there. She may pull out early. I'll meet you here 'fore she does."

He hurried away into the darkness.

We spread out, kicking, feeling around in what we thought were likely places. I couldn't seem to find anything that was even wooden till I came upon a little sawmill below the tracks. I fell off of a narrow walk in it but landed in a sawdust pile. From there I saw a square shape, tumbled at one end and silhouetted in the light from town. Being in the sawdust I wondered if I was under the saw and if I might, in raising up, split my head open on the sharp teeth. Then I saw it quite close to me and I reached over the sawdust remover chute and felt one of its sharp teeth. Overhead the roof of the open-sided mill loomed black in the dark sky and the sawdust was dry under my feet. Ever since I've always felt that sawmills are somehow cozy. I reached over and rapped the big disc of steel with my knuckles and it rang like a temple gong. Then I remembered what I came for and searched some more, but everything that was wooden was nailed down. I was heading back when I saw that the dark shape before me was a stack of long slabwood. I ran to find Glen and together we made four trips from stack to car before Max and the old man came through the gloom. Max had a piece of tarpaper torn from a shed and the old man had two immense cardboard boxes. Wordlessly, he slit the boxes at the corners and laid them flat over the hole. Then we laid the slabs side by side, flat side down, over that, and Max turned his paper, dry side up, for us to sit on. Glen helped the old man up and we crawled up after, thankful that the trainman had been too busy on the other side of the freight to see our activity.

In Alder Point you couldn't tell the storm existed: the place was walled away in a deep hole in the redwoods where mist and moss clung to everything, including quite probably the folks. The train didn't start, and Glen and I got out and re-lieved ourselves and did setting up exercises to get our blood circulating and then crawled up into our tunnel where I again tackled the bindings on my pack and soon had my floored lean-to miner's tent loose. We worked around till we were sitting in it side by side, riding backwards again. The tent sidewalls covered each outside man from the slip stream of the train, and its top swept up our backs from its sewn-in floor and went over our heads and out to our feet before us.

"We better not smoke or light matches," I said. "I water-proofed this tent with linseed oil, beeswax and paraffin." Right away I was hungry for a smoke.

"Rigged out like we planned it," said the old man.

Glen laughed: "Little different than back there on the ties. I began to think I'd never make Salt Lake."

"Why Salt Lake?"

"I figgered and figgered," said the boy, "and read in lots of books, and I chose Salt Lake for where I'd start."

"That's a long pull," I said, "over the Sierras in the winter. Too bad you haven't got enough dough to ride over the hump in a passenger coach—say a matter of four bucks." Ruefully I thought of my seven cents.

"Yeah," the boy rejoined, "but Papa said, 'Make your own way, Carl'—he never would call me Glen—'Make your own way but never buy it. Only way is to earn.' He had that framed in the shop."

I smiled—to myself, I thought—at how closely the boy's description matched my picture of it, but my smugness must have shown.

"You'll do," the old man said to me.

"How do you know?"

"I don't savvy why," he said, "but I feel that as an anti-cipator you've caught something. Now you're feeling pleased with yourself," he said. "Remember, anticipators are a dime a dozen."

The locomotive up the track hooted and wailed through the night. I felt the redwoods took it to their brittle, stately cores. And the river too, I felt, didn't deflect those sounds from its gliding bosom, but roiled them in with its currents and—along with everything else, even gold—bore some of it to the sea. Why to the sea, why not away? I asked myself. *You sound like an arty bastard—"some of it to the sea"—ya-a-ah.* Well, how about the black sands on these coasts? They've got gold in them that was brought down by rivers like this one. *Maybe it was washed up from under the sea.* Uh, uh, you can't wash gold uphill—it's heavy. It filters down, never up.

With a jerk that came crashing down the line of cars we began to move. The flat wheels made their sound slowly, softly. Like the Queen's carriage over the cobbles of London Town, we rolled to the tie noises. Presently the rhythm lost stateliness: the flat wheels began to tap out the increased speed of their revolutions and the cars to rack and groan as they coursed poorly-laid rails. We were under way. Far ahead the engine cast its wail deep into the forest once more and, as it did so, turned a curve so that the last of it was muted as if begging no echo.

"We're rolling now, Grandpa," said Max from his side of the car. "Pony up that drink."

"The way to make it last," said the old man, "is to wait until the next station and then one more."

"With you guys hogging in on it? That's a laugh! Come on, pony up!"

The old man stirred around and finally handed him the bottle. "Act cute with it and I'll break your arm."

"You're gonna have to prove that right now," Max snarled.

"It's your arm." The old man's voice was inflexible.

"I half believe you would."

"You know it."

The bottle came meekly back. I took a little snort.

"Still feel the same?" I asked Glen.

"Ain't tempted now," he laughed. "I feel better."

I handed the bottle back to the old man.

"We'll take your share, boy," he said. "What's in your kit?"

"Shoemaking tools," answered the boy. "I make shoes by hand same as Papa."

"Where'd your old man learn the trade?"

"Why, Switzerland, of course. The best comes from there."

"Sure," agreed the old man jovially, "best watches and milk goats, now you add shoes."

Glen, I imagined, was a young man without guile or humor. I realized he'd stick to his last because his temperament wouldn't urge him beyond it. Don't sneer, I said to myself—he'll be a superb craftsman, come much closer to real art with his nose to the grindstone than you ever will at your far-flung verse.

Strange, I thought, one of us chasing madly after things not truly seen or known; the other setting out sturdily, secure in improving his rather simple task—carving, curving, shaping until the boot has grace, true grace, the thing you seek everywhere and find so fleeting. But I knew definitely down deep that I was right for me. Pay it to the wind, I told myself, for goods received. He'll never breach those summits for a glance of where we've wantoned for hours. Yes, I meant we—the accumulate, the composite, the husband, searcher, fool and, deep in the silliness of us, a student of the anatomy of enigma. Mystic, even—one of those words that puts my back hair up, describing a type of person I despise—Mr. Sludge, the medium! Let it go, the calm part of me said, let it slide.

No wind came through our floor and the rain and sleet that rattled in from time to time were things to be observed, not felt. The heat of our bodies and of our breath filled the strange haven and slighted under the edge that covered our feet, so that the air was neither stagnant nor humid. After Max on the other side of the old man begged another snort and, downing it, curled up against him and began to snore, I too fell asleep sitting up. It was one of those sleeps where the resting and recuperating usual in eight hours are completed in one or two. I believe I slept an hour and a half at most and awoke lying on my back.

I was aware that Glen and the old man sitting on either side of me were awake in the dark. We banged and lurched, but this car was better than most. It glided over the rails with its heavy burden of green ties while we, though still wet and worn, took our ease. Some mist we were passing through laid the engine smoke low along the river and strands of it ravelled under our tent and came to our nostrils with the primal smell of steamships and locomotives, the exhalation of big travel. Under way, I thought, going somewhere, going home! The locomotive up ahead sent its cry out before it as a challenge that drifted back over us. The old man was talking to Glen, calling him "son" without the least condescension, giving it warmth. Son, said out of patriarch's beard in the dark, can be a rich thing when he who says it has his own teeth, and judging from the way he handled his consonants the old man had his.

"Son," he said, "how about these shoes?"

Well, the boy didn't say much for awhile but finally he began talking about them, about the lasts and about good leather. He seemed to like the word supple: supple leather, supple hands, and the supple insteps of the people who wore the handmade shoes. Though when he spoke of the arch of the foot it was high, keystoned rigidly with metatarsals. I relished his two incompatible views of one thing. He seemed to feel that he had to go out amongst us Americans and show us as his father had what wonderful people the Swiss are. Don't know how they got that into him at home, but he had it, though it was all wound up with shoes and religion.

It's funny how frail fellows like Glen, these almost translucent-bodied people with their narrow chests and ways can show a determination utterly masculine that hardier men seldom possess. It's something of the psyche or the soul of the man certainly, because there wasn't bone nor meat nor mind enough within the boy to house such a feeling. He was telling us how he helped his father soak the leather before they made a shoe and of the wooden lasts his father made in the shape of individual feet, of the wood he carved them from and how he boiled them in linseed oil so they wouldn't swell or crack. Glen thought it was dangerous to do it in the house.

"It catches on fire sometimes," he said. "You have to watch it in a little shop like that. Often we worked in the kitchen. It was warm there and we saved on fuel. We didn't get a great deal for our shoes, not as much as we should, but we were kind of proud of that. Us Schweitzers were giving them more than they paid for."

"So now you're taking your little kit and heading for the big city to get a job with some custom shoe outfit," said the old man.

"I'd like to start out," Glen said, "in a big wide city that was clean. They say Salt Lake City is clean. I don't know about the Mormons. Still, they're kinda Christly, I guess, though not enough to be saved. The straight way is really narrow, but they aim at the Way. They're trying to be part of His flock. From how I hear they laid out their city, I'd like to make shoes for them. They say—at least in the geographies at school—that the streets are broad and shaded with trees— lindens, maybe, like Ma talks about being in Europe—and maybe they wouldn't rush around there the way we do in Eureka. With that nippy wind coming in from the sea you got to keep moving most of the time. I'd like to make shoes for people to wear as they sauntered down broad, shaded walks, not spiked logging shoes or leather dairy boots, but shoes worn when folks took their ease and came down off of their porches for a warm, easy walk and felt the shoes on their feet was just right for it. I'd use wood pegs in the heels so they didn't make too much noise. Can't stand rubber heels myself— it kinda takes something out of the shoe, the something that Papa was putting in—but I don't like the nails sounding in the shoes either. But with the maple pegs—why, I can almost hear the sound, and people could get used to me making their shoes. I could make a lot of them, get a shop started, hire all Swiss. No, not all Swiss either—there's other people. My father says some Swedes make good shoes. I'd like him to come there too, after we got the trade started buying those supple fine-grained shoes up there."

I lay listening, knowing that a kaleidoscope of linden shade, finely shod feet, and a general air of rustic refinement was brushing by the backs of Glen's eyes, and as I further tried to imagine what he saw, he spoke again wistfully. "I'd certainly like to get started in Salt Lake City."

The old man was silent and Glen didn't say anything more. I felt he was staring into the darkness, still intent on his objectives. But after a time he slowly slumped, folding into sleep. The old man told him to hunker down and snooze easy while he could. When Glen laid down I sat up and tried to find something in my pack to put over him, but the down sleeping bag and all clothing were completely sodden. When we rounded a sharp turn and the rails squealed under the stubborn, unturning trucks, he trembled and muttered what sounded like a fragment of a prayer.

"Believe you slept over an hour," the old man said to me. "How do you feel?"

"Hungry and tired. I was four days getting to the railroad."

"Here's three figs," he said. "I only got six. Chew 'em slow and let the seeds stick in your teeth. You got any cavities?"

"A couple."

"Fine!" he said. "You let some of the pulp and seeds get caught in the cavities, then in an hour or so you work a little pulp with your tongue. It makes a might fine little morsel and gives you the feeling you've done something, and the seeds—you find them one at a time and crack 'em with your front teeth."

He got the figs into my hand after some fumbling and I bit down frugally on my first food since two goin' on three days.

"What's the country you came out of like?"

"Steep," I answered. "Plenty of game with here and there a shake cabin abandoned God knows when."

"Brushy?"

"No, it's a country of great sugar pines and fir. Way too much shade. The tall lines of the trunks of trees hide how chopped-up the country is. And no women. Oh, there's the storekeeper's wife at Emby. She's sixty-five at least."

"Wonder if I could stay put in a place like that."

"I couldn't. I wasn't making much more than grub money. The river was too high, but that ain't what drove me out. Anyway, I got a family down on the Bay—and darn glad, for I saw a fella up there who had stayed too long."

"Keep talking," the old man said, almost irritably. Later I was to know, it was avidly. "We're gonna be on this car until morning and I'm tired of my own thoughts and can't sleep."

I thought of telling him of my unfinished poem, but quickly decided against it.

"Come on," he said, "tell me about this chopped up country."

"Well," I said, "I've told you. I was prospecting up there, and this in winter, and on top of it all I was green at it. I keep marveling I'm here at all considering the stupid things I've done on this trek..."

So I began telling him about the country and about my puny attempts at prospecting, the details of my trip working themselves loose from my memory like so many fig seeds.

I'd been up on the Pell River—that's a tributary of the Siskiyou. I'd camped way up the river in an old deserted prospector's cabin whose builder, from the looks of things, must have been touched in the head. When I packed into the country it was early November and only Hoss Mountain and Snider's Peak had snow on them, but two weeks later all the timberline country was snowed in solid. Then with each storm —and that was twice a day sometimes—the snowline crept down until only the gorges and valleys were green. When the wind blew down from Muletail Basin, where the Pell had its source, it left no doubt in your mind that winter was about to clog the mountains high and low and till spring.

Well, I knew I'd have to lay in enough grub for the winter snow-up or get out, so I got out—maybe because my hands

43

were pretty near useless from panning in the icy water, swollen and stiff, so that I couldn't button the fly of my pants or roll a cigarette. The snow was within half a mile of my cabin when I left. After I'd gone several miles down the river trail—going farther and farther from Virgin Creek, the place where I knew I'd find gold but never got to—I came to a primitive dam in the river from where a flume clinging to the wall of the canyon carried its race of water down to Emby.

Emby was a little mining town about seven miles below. Town, did I say? It was a log cabin store and post office that got its supplies by pack horse from the road forty miles down on the Siskiyou River, but it was all the town there was to forty or fifty prospectors who were scattered in the region of a hundred square miles or so.

Below Emby there were several hydraulic mining operations that never paid. There was gold of a sort in the country, but no rich strikes were made. Most of the operations were carried on by mining companies who were more interested in selling stock than in garnering gold from the gravel bars of the Pell River. It is a wild, uprearing country with its forests growing from land that is seldom far from perpendicular, and scattered through this topsy-turvy wilderness were a handful of lonely men filled with dreams and beans, some of them cabin-crazy and unable to care for themselves, drifting half-dead here and there, scratching in crevices in the bedrock and churning at the gravel painfully. It had been going on a long time—mining was one of the first things that brought the white man to California.

I later found that the Virgin Creek I longed to get to had first been mined in the seventies by a great company of Chinamen who threw their tailings out on both sides of the creek so that when they left, Virgin Creek ran like a sluice down a bedrock bed to the Pell. Later another mining company packed in the long uphill miles and worked the tailings over again and threw them from each side back into the very center of the stream as they worked. When they left, Virgin Creek ran down both sides of the tailings as two sluices, straight down, where it had once careened and rested in pools on its way to the Pell.

The long plank that led over the dam to the flume was a problem. Spray from the falls had blown up over it and had frozen, covering it and rounding it with transparent glaze, and in its new dimension it was a dangerous thing to cross. I got down on my hands and knees and inched along it, high up over the roaring falls. About half way across, my packboard with its seventy pounds of duffel slid up my back and hit me a crashing blow at the base of my skull, but I hung on and got it back where it belonged and finally gained the walkway on the edge of the flume. The walk was only a foot wide with no rail. If you fell, you fell into the flume, where the water was running so fast that you could never stop yourself before you either drowned or dropped down into the Pell's canyon one hundred feet or so to the rocks. You didn't look close down before you to see where to put your feet as you walked, but looked ahead, letting the instincts handle immediate footing, and watched for the overhanging brush from the cliffside, so that it wouldn't catch the load you were carrying and spill you from the narrow plank.

There'd been a lot of little towns come and go down on the river that the Pell ran into—little prospector towns: Gold City, Burnt Corral, and Chinzy. Each one had its strong man, its dream of growing and of future wealth, and some had grown, like Whiskey Hill and Oretown. I thought of this as I walked along, to keep from getting nervous and maybe freezing and losing my rhythm and with it my sense of balance and too soon after, quite probably, my sense of life. I thought of those wrecks of ghost towns and of the melancholy and sadness that one felt wandering their ruins.

In the twilight I finished my dizzy trek on the flume and hit the trail, for the canyon I'd been traversing broadened and its slopes were becoming gentle enough to support here and there a tree, and there was room for the trail alongside the river.

45

Then through another narrows with the twilight deepening I came down to where the canyon widened again as two streams came in, one from each side, to join the Pell, and there, surrounded by towering cliffs, were maybe ten acres of a brushy little flat. I was about to pass through, walking over a great bar of gravel of some acres in extent, when I saw a man in the dusk of the cliffs.

I went over to him. He stood there with a look of melancholy searching on his face. Like a hound, he seemed to be testing the atmosphere of the place. He was a dumpy little fellow, built something like a top, except that his shoulders were very narrow and sloping. He didn't seem to have any waist at all and his belly overhung his pants so much that neither of us could see his belt. He still wore that look of speculative wonder as I approached, but then in the deep twilight of the place I saw it change to one of vested authority. He gave me the feeling that he was sure he was of a higher stratum of society than I could aspire to, but he was tolerant. This was America and he knew it just as I did, and even conceiving the great gulf that separated us he gave me a friendly smile and said, "I bet you don't know where you're standing right now." I agreed.

"You're standing in the town of Corby. Of course," he explained, "we haven't been able to get the pipe up for the flumes yet. You understand, it takes time to develop an extensive bar such as you see here, but they's a new road being run over the hills from Waddle and the Gillsips brothers is puttin' in machinery just six miles below here, so it's just a matter of time before we have residences on both sides of the street. What bothers me, though, and never seems to bother Pa—" And here he forgot what bothered him and went on saying of his father, "He drove his stakes for this town forty years ago when I was a young 'un and he's just bidin' his time knowin' that it's sure to happen and the rest of the world'll ketch up with his idea. He's sayin' lately that if I'll stick by he'll will a hefty chunk of it to me, as if I'd leave after all

46

Pa's been through—like Ma a dyin' that winter she stepped on a slippery peel the pig missed. She spoke accusin' of Pa towards the last, but wimmin can never size up mining proper, Pa says, and I could see she didn't know the value of the bar. Still, if I could get control someday it would be a good thing, cuz I been studying how to run a little city and got a lot of brand new plans on how to do it slick as a whistle."

He paused, not to let me talk, but to take in that forlorn landscape. "A little city in God's country here," he went on, "—ain't that gonna be wonderful. Pa's gettin' so old he don't see the beauty in it no more, waitin' so tarnation long you get to take it for granted. He owns the whole bar along here, ya know. It's on the government maps that way: Corby's Bar. And there used to be a dot on the map right about where we're standin' to show there was a cabin here, but a fella brought a woman up here into the mining country and they lived in the cabin. We always knew no good would come of it. He was doin' some preliminary panning for Pa on shares and sure enough they burned the cabin down one night tryin' to get a fire big enough in the fireplace, so she could see to take a tick outta the small of his back. He was a awful hairy fella and I guess she was usin' a comb tryin' to make a part in him to find where the tick was hid, it bitin' on a nerve meanwhile, I guess. It got real bright in the cabin and she was doin' fine. She got it out, head and all, without puttin' coal oil on it, just by turnin' it opposite way from a clock, and they was congratulating each other what a good job she done when they noticed the cabin's whole end, along with the ceiling, was afire. We never done no buildin' here since. Live down at Emby."

He seemed to have lost the thread of his story, but picked it up momentarily: "But, like I say, what bothers me is—if we get quite a town started here before the highway gets up to it, shouldn't we run our street where we figger the highway's gonna come, so's not to make too much of a jog? Or will the highway people make a big swing as they come into town and join our street head-on, so nothin' will look gimcrack?"

As he said this he looked down that street of his, un-encumbered by the ominous grandeur of great cliffs that overhung his little flat. Down there in the canyon we stood in deep gloom, almost darkness. But looking up I could see, high above us where the mountains slanted away into the last yellow light, that trees had fingered into crevasses up there and, gripping tightly, had found resource in the rock—not gold, of course, but enough so they could hold on and build a bough or two, even support some cones. After I'd looked at them for a bit, he didn't seem so strange as he had.

"Yup, I'm Jim Corby's son," he was saying, "and glad to show you our properties here. I come pretty near every day, lookin' her over and checkin' on things. Pa's usually round Smither's store down at Emby. You might stop and talk to him if you know of any big mining companies that would like to get onto a bar of high-grade gravel, cuz Pa's been lookin' for a de-velopment like that for a good many years." He paused, and then added with quiet and sad dignity, "And I hunger to see it happen too while I'm still in my prime."

I could hardly see his face as I left him, but now, as I recounted the story to the old man, I could conjure up Jim Corby's son clearly, and tried to do him justice: "In the start, he'd been a little bit on the brag, but as his tale progressed he came closer to me. And at the last he was standing on tip toe right before me. Staring into my eyes beseechingly. Hoping that through me, as he had hoped of the few others he'd accosted on this trail through the years, he could get news to the outside where the big mining operators came from—news that would incite them to come up to Emby and help in the opening up and development of Corby's Bar."

When I finished, the old man was silent for awhile, then he said: "I gotta admit that was a pretty slick yarn."

"It's funny," I mused aloud, "I didn't mean it to be. I thought about it on the way out, saw it as a start of a story I might write. S'pose I was thinking how it'd look on paper and not how it would sound to anyone else."

Max spoke up loudly: "Hell! We got a goddamned genius amongst us." He dragged himself into a sitting position. "You think I don't know. You think I'm some poor bastard brought up in a lousy orphanage, don't you? And you think you're a pretty knowing cookie. Sure, I seen it in your eyes. But me, no-good Max, I'm tellin' ya, you're crude. Yeah, I know I am, but forget that for a minute and take a gander at you. You're a wincer, yeah, your whole tribe is. You belong to the 'Oh no, not that' school. You're sensitive, only I spell it s-o-f-t. Think I ain't got the cases to know? Listen I had a sister was an artist till she flipped her lid. My old man's home is in Walla Walla. It was a fine Orthodox Jewish home, so I don't have to tell you who's the blacksheep. My sister she gets artistic but heavy and pretty soon she's gotta leave Walla Walla. Nothing would do but New York. The family was proud. They had maybe a genius in the house. My father was botherin' everybody about the number of geniuses in Jewish families. He figured it out percentage-wise.

"She started in with watercolors of cats, then it was still-lifes in oils. By the time she left for New York she was a poetess and every goddamned thing she did was screwed up—her walk and her talk and her clothes and her goddamned thought were all tampered with. Even the way she did her hair was lousy. She was always yapping about life, but she couldn't touch the gow of it no more. Hell no, she'd touch the wand of her sensibilities to the edge of the gow and then write about lusty, piquant life. Don't worry a Jew's wise to you prissy ones. They get a big play in our families. Hell, genius sprawled on the dollar is our coat of arms, but you're not even a kike and here you are mouthing this line of scabby significance. Well, it's just so goddamned much crum and you and me both know it."

The old man waited for my reaction. When it didn't come, he said: "What's a matter, Willie? You takin' our beefs with no fight at all?"

"If you mean about my story," I said, "you're talking about something I'll be trying to improve, and your knocks are useful to me. About the other, I'll get down next stop beside the tracks and if there's any little thing anybody don't like about the shape of my nose, come down."

"You got a lotta mouth."

"Jump down next stop."

"Sounds like you're only soft in places," the old man said quizzically. "Max, if I was you I'd stay up off that ballast next stop. It's the soft-spot hard-spot guys that kill."

"We'll see," answered Max.

I don't care either way, I thought, only I've got to be careful. Got to keep my hands off his throat, got to keep headed toward Nordi's arms, not a noose.

We pounded along. No sound came from my companions. I got to imagining we were passing through broad fields. I knew we weren't, but still the feeling persisted: rolling fields of wheat full of blackbirds. It was strange how the idea remained in my mind.

I MUST HAVE FALLEN asleep and when I awoke both Max and the old man were snoring gently and the boy muttered in his dreams. I tried to go to sleep again but couldn't and that feeling of passing through rolling uplands of wheat kept claiming my inner eye, even though the canyon wall often blasted back the sounds of our passing.

For awhile I pictured how a breakfast would be when I was once more a family man: oatmeal with Bessie's cream and little Bunky solemnly spooning it out of his bowl and studying me as each spoon reached his mouth, then looking modestly down in his bowl as he chewed and dipped up the next spoonful. I remembered how it felt when he hugged me around the neck. I was his "Da." I was in a ferment to breach the space between us and be home with them. If only I were almost there, only a mile more and then they'd both be hugging me, clinging to me, laughing and kissing, and we'd be saying our special words to one another. "Who's the pots and pans man?" I'd say, and Bunk would rush me all fists and giggling fury. "I'm the pots and pans man!" he'd howl and belabor my knees.

After a time the scenes of my goal began to grow dim, though I tried vainly to furbish them. I saw Nordi and the boy, it seemed, from a distance. We passed the roar of a waterfall and I glanced that way, and when I stared back their way once more they were gone.

I bit down on a seed or two of the figs. Hunger somehow didn't bother me now. Perhaps the business of going home held it in abeyance. Things hadn't been so bad. Oh, that sleet had been rough, but sleet had dogged me even on my way into the mountains.

Take the evening of the second day in from Eureka. I was plodding along bone tired, my big packboard with its load riding me down. Far below me a river sounded its muffled roar, though I could not see it for the mist that filled the valley. Off to the side and a little below the road was the sound of a leaping brook that passed through a stand of big hemlocks. I was about to leave the road and head down to make my camp there when it started to sleet, and with the sleet came a truck heading my way. It stopped beside me. In the cab sat a gaunt man, one of the kind for whom work is a hopeless addiction, and a woman of middle age. Jammed into the cab with them was a girl of perhaps seventeen whose eyelids were inflamed with pinkeye. I never saw her again.

"Where you goin' in this damn weather?" the man wanted to know.

"Up the Pell," I answered. I looked at his load: on the flat bed truck was one layer of boxed goods over which a tarp had been roped. The narrow steel tailgate was bare of boxes.

"Tailgate's all I've got to offer. Can you ride it?" he asked me. Then before I could answer: "I got to git goin'. You comin?"

I heaved my pack on the tailgate, crawled up beside it, and looked for handholds as we swung around the next turn. Soon it was dark. The road was crooked and uneven; a dozen times I was almost thrown from my narrow perch before I succeeded in tying my pack to the ropes of the load. Then I grabbed a tight one and let my hands clamp on it. For the next hour we twisted and turned through a downpour laced with hail. Then the truck stopped at a lighted house, the first one on the journey.

Three old men limped from it and helped the driver unload the truck. The rain poured down steadily. They had to lift me down: I couldn't get off the truck myself, my legs cramped from cold and the one position. Then they asked me inside and brought my pack in and stood it in a corner. The boxes of merchandise once disposed of in a storeroom, the men came back.

We stood about a big stove set almost in the center of the room. It glowed red in the dim lamplight.

"Haul up a chair and set down," the man who had driven the truck said.

I stood drying the seat of my pants by the fire. No one spoke for a long while. The old men spat from time to time into the woodbox and the pitchy knot in the stove snapped and outside rain fell in a steady torrent.

Finally the truck driver—who, from his manner, owned the place—thumbed the quid of snooze from his lower lip and flung it neatly into the woodbox. "He figgers to prospect up the Pell," he said.

We all sat in the vague lamplight in poses of deep concentration. But they said nothing. I felt they considered it from every angle. Finally I became sure that they were waiting for me to confirm the report, but I stubbornly kept dumb. The silence lengthened unbearably and I decided I was being very rude. "That," I said—I was choked up. It sounded like the call of a night heron, but I tried again and got it out. "That's right," I said.

At once they moved around in their chairs and considered me with bright, infinitely comprehending eyes and then glanced to one another shrewdly. "Young fella here goin' up the Pell, doin' a little pannin' on his lonesome"—oh, it was in the air, but no one said it. The fire popped and one man went to work and shoved his big, blunt hands into his pants' pockets and straightened his legs out before him and stared at his boots and still nobody said anything. For me—well, I couldn't keep it up. I'm a mouth, so I let it fling.

"I hear there's platinum in your gold up here." I was satisfied with that. It sounded—well, it sounded to me like I was one of them. I chewed a little on my tongue. How can one ruminate without quid, cud, or bovine mind? I chewed on my tongue. "Heard it's lighter!" I remarked.

That started them.

"Hearin's one thing," said an old fellow in the corner whom I hadn't noticed. "I'd say they's about the same 'cept the white stuff's flakier." He raised his cracked voice then as if addressing quite a party along with myself: "If it's platinum you're after you shoulda headed up the Trinity 'stead a here, and the Pell's the same as this here Siskiyou when it comes to white gold."

"I don't really care about the color. I'm after any of it."

"Too late to cross the pass," he cracked on from his corner. "Snow six foot deep by now and rotten spots in it to drown you. No place for man or beast this fur into winter. Have to go around by the coast to pan platinum on the Trinity and whut fur anyway? Ain't enough there if you worried it out to keep you in Clabber Girl Baking Powder, let alone beans. Who put you up to this white gold prospectin' anyhow, young fella?"

"No one. I just heard and was inquiring."

"Well, I wouldn't trust him," the old man went on, getting more aroused and huffy with each word.

"Dinner'll be ready in a jiffy," the owner said, coming over to me. "We're sort of a restaurant with rooms—a inn, I aim it to be. We'll lay a place for you."

"Thank you," I replied too quickly. "I'll just dry a little bit and get along. I've got to do my own cooking."

"Set up camp on a night like this?" he asked. "Why, it's all afloat out there. Come on, dinner's only forty cents and the beef's real beef I bought in Eureka."

"But I've got to watch every cent until I get started," I mumbled. I was woefully low on cash.

54

"Forty cents ain't gonna sink ya," he answered wrathfully. "I'd give you the meal only the place's got to pay her way. These three," he indicated the old-timers, "is boardin' out the winter 'stead a goin' cabin crazy up the Pell. You can't prospect in the winter, Bucko. How come you're up here anyway?"

"I'm interested in the second benches," I answered with much dignity and a knowing air.

But he burst out laughing in my face. "Bet ya got one of them theories, uh? Well, come on to dinner. You'd pay seventy cents for this forty-cent dinner down in Eureka or Willits. It's got lotsa beef fat in it. Ain't no buck tallow off a sidehill salmon in this stew."

He moved to a door behind which the clatter of dishes had been going on and the old men rose to follow. Two were so stove up it was a rickety business. "Coxie Army," I said to myself. Then the door opened to reveal a stout woman who blew the hair out of her eyes, looking crosseyed at the process as she did so.

"No you don't, Elmer," she bleated richly. "Ya ain't to come till I holler. Best back up and sit down. I've run into a little trouble."

"Hell, Ruthie, we're hongry," Elmer mourned. "Here I drive clean down to Arcata and back gettin' needins and I bring back beef fat for you to fling in that venison stew to make it legal and you doin' nothin' practically 'cept hold up the parade."

"Come when I call," the woman said from behind the door she had closed. "'Member, we been all over how we do this part. Can't run no hotel ever which way."

"If she wasn't always so thirsty, I'd say she was a camel," growled Elmer as we found our old places.

"Camels is got a hump," remarked one of the cripples.

"Well, maybe she ain't all camel," agreed our host, "but she's all hump."

He took some receipts from his pocket and studied them. He seemed to get a lot out of his remark or the receipts. Anyway, he raised the wick on the lamp and opened the kitchen door, and in the better light I could see the room and the boarders. The place smelled of pine pitch and fir pitch and wet woolens that had been dried over smoky fires. The whole place was made of new rough lumber with an eye to simulating knotty pine, much used to simulate new rough lumber, so that making a full cycle through concept it outdistanced affectation and arrived back at what it was. On one side of the room they had tried to shellac the wall but quit after about a quart, I estimated. These magazines about beautifying the home get into the damndest places!

I sat down in an old rocker whose leather seat was worn away leaving a round hole—sort of a rocking privy seat. I wondered if Monkey Ward's had such a piece of paraphernalia in their catalog. The old man next to me was sitting deep down in the hole of another rocker with a harried look, as if he were going to ask for assistance before he was completely trapped by the seat. Instead, he gasped out that up the Pell the second benches were lean pickins unless you found bedrock up there. "Anywhere on bedrock, least bedrock up the Pell, you're liable to come on a crack and if you get to the bottom of it you'll maybe come on more than just color." Here he gave me a look of such terrific knowingness that it almost ruptured his face.

On the other side of the stove sat one of his cronies. He was a big, strong-looking fellow, his immense paws knotted by a lifetime of panning in icy waters. He was trimming the warped and fluted horn of his fingernails in the better light. Finally he reared back the great bald head he had been presenting to us and fixed me with a solemn appraisal. "Which side of the Pell you going up, lad?" he growled.

I remembered my map. Virgin Creek flowed in from the west side—Virgin Creek, just waiting for me with its nuggets.

"Why, the east side is what I figured on," I said softly. "That way I'll get the early morning light."

He stared at me up and down till I felt foolish because my boot laces were cloth, not the rawhide of self-respecting prospectors. When he went back to his horn-chipping I was much relieved.

Covertly I studied these three beat-up old boys. None of them looked as if he'd gone through two or three big fortunes in his life; they had the air of men who could perhaps wear through the heel of a sock with more elan. They didn't have the hacking cough that I felt would be attendant to a lifetime trafficking in gold dust. I was beginning to wonder, but put it brusquely aside. The Pell's probably nugget country and these old boys misers, never using an ounce of their hoardings. I thought it as stoutly as I could. Guess I was apprehensive. Probably built the idea to lean on.

Since I'd gotten off the truck the wind had-been rising. We seemed to be down between two mountains where the river's roar could be heard faintly in the lulls. The downpour that had followed us up the Siskiyou must have been only the vanguard, for now the house shook and creaked under the storm's assault. Rain drummed on the roof and beat at the windows until I felt I was seeing a movie where the sound effects man had gone mad. Wind shook the door, and outside some loose battens that hadn't been nailed down properly whanged at the wall as if seeking entry.

"I'd a made this house with studdings and herringbone braces," said the big fellow, scraping horribly on a twisted fingernail that reminded me of a crumpled horn of a cow. "Board and batten is all right for a cabin, but this big place you've built here moves with the wind like it was drunk." He peered at my cloth laces. "Heard that down in the city they got laws on how to do it, so you don't get crushed under your own carpentry. That so?" He raised his eyes and gave me that gimlet glance again.

"Yep," I replied at once, "they've got codes."

"Trouble with you," Elmer said to the big man, "you never built nothing but dams and flumes and chinked-up miner shacks. Every room I add to this is a block, just like a block of wood, and it's piled against the rest making them all stronger. Sure she weaves a little, made of green lumber and all, but when she's settled and painted on the outside and another room added over the storeroom, she'll be as solid as Wenlowe's stone garage in Eureka."

I listened to a gust coming up the river, crowding into the funnel of the hills. When it hit the house, horizontal cloudburst and all, I felt the place move on its foundations. It ripped a piece of roofing off, for we heard it go clattering up to the peak, where it took off—a tarpaper witch minus her broomstick. Where the paper had been rain soon fell through to the ceiling and then through it to the floor. Elmer left to "rassle me a bucket," as he put it, and came back with three, which he set in the growing puddle on the floor. They caught most of the drips, but some of the water ran along a board in the ceiling until it could drop-drop on the stove, and the stove fried each drop as it lit.

"Shakes 'ud never done that," the prospector mused.

"'Course, and shakes take time, which I didn't have," answered Elmer. "It'll be a shake roof when I'm through with it. Move that little pail over to the new drip," he said to me. As I did, the fat woman stood monumental in the light of the kitchen door.

"The meal's ready," she cried. "I even rubbed up a cherry pie. Elmer brung a number ten tin of 'em from the food auction. Come an' eat while it's hot."

My reverie received a painful shock. Glen rolled over in his sleep and kicked me hard on the chin. As I rubbed it and cursed under my breath I noticed the others still snored softly. And here I am, I thought, with strangers in another stormy night and with the jar and rattle of the freight to boot. Going home though now—that makes it different. Different sure, but not essentially better. Moving toward adventure and possible good fortune should be just as heady as the return to family, and the trip up the Pell had in retrospect been heady, if tinged with melancholy. I had so little to go on—twelve dollars it was—and the winter and the rain were depressing. There was a little forlornness too, maybe, for I hadn't been away from family and friends for several years and as I plodded toward the mountains they seemed to be defying me to enter their gorges.

That meal I had at Elmer's place has now largely disappeared from my memory. I remember vaguely how the old prospectors crouched over their big bowls of stew, though they went about their eating in the patient manner of draft animals; how that mountain of a woman took a liking to me and, after I'd consumed two helpings of the stew, purposely arranged the lamp so that I could see at the back of the long room a soda bar and fountain, taken in one piece from a cleaner, happier home. I was amused at the incongruousness of its marble top and varnished mahogany in this place.

"Elmer got it cheap," she said to me. "Ain't it pretty?"

"Had to set it out five feet from the wall so she could get behind it," said Elmer, coming up out of his bowl at a time when he shouldn't have been talking.

And then for some damn reason she felt she had to make me a soda.

"Got the water pressure to make it foam," she said. "I'll put some sody in it and it will." She went to the door and scooped up a handful of hail that had bounced off the roof. She whirled this around with some soda and a little vinegar in the can that had the cherries in it—"fer flavor," she said—poured in some canned milk and stirred it under one of the gleaming taps while the pressured water shot its thin stream into the suds it made. At once there was an awful pounding and clatter. The floor shook as some machine, worn loose to the point of flying to pieces, tried once more to do what it had been built to do and had done for the last twenty-five years.

"It's the pump and compressor Elmer got at the auction," the lady yelled at me over the racket. I waited apprehensively with the old men for the machine to blow up. "It's under the counter," she screamed on, "with the exhaust pipe going through the wall. Keeps up our water pressure for our fountain, but we got no tank, so they ain't no reserve. The compressor'll give us air for tires when we get the station built." She passed me the drink in a Mason jar. "Haven't got the glasses yet, but then the trade don't start till May up here."

I tried to quaff it as the complex, worn out machinery went on, intent on shaking itself to pieces, and all the while that mound of a woman beaming at me. The men didn't glance my way. I felt it was a lofty decency on their parts, and finally downed the distressing concoction. Then I banged the Mason jar down hard on the counter, so they could hear it above the racket and know that my trial was over and take their eyes from their bowls and look about.

"Thank you," I said to the lady, "thank you kindly."

I don't remember when the pump and engine quit, though I suppose it did when it got the pressure up and was still in one piece.

Back in the room by the stove I began to draw the prospectors out on the country and about methods of getting gold and game. All this to the plink-plunk of water dripping in the buckets and the s-psst of the drops frying on the stove. The little old guy was back in his bottomless rocker, jammed into it so that he was nearly sitting on the floor, though rocking furiously. He was a hound for bedrock.

"When the gold gets down to bedrock it can't go no farther, and when it gets in a cranny in the bedrock it stays till hell freezes over or the right man comes along. Remember that, young feller."

The big prospector leaned out of his ancient Morris chair, snapped his jack knife shut and impaled me on that glance of his. The little guy saw he was going to say something and sank even farther into the seat of his rocker, literally fanning the floor with his froglike prat.

"Why is the bars got names to 'em up here—tell me that!" said the big man. "Soames Bar, Corby's Bar, and Split-Tongue Bar—is any of the crannies in the bedrock payin' enough so's they got names to 'em? Nossir. Up here if a guy's a man he gets on to a bar of gravel that a day's pannin' shows has got the makings and he hacks himself out a rocker and riffle and goes to work moving yardage. Yeah, and leaves this minin' with tablespoon and whiskbroom to men a no git." He spat and then sat back staring at the ceiling.

The little guy's face worked as he rocked on. He was building up a dinger of a rejoinder when the front door swung open and a young man and young woman with a vast amount of wild, wet air made their entrance. The wind blew the door to the kitchen open and Elmer came erect from behind the counter, a monkey wrench in his hand, slipped on something, and grasped one of the gleaming spigots, which shot its clever stream of water downward. At once the gas engine and pump started to shake and rattle as it tried to hammer a little more pressure into the pipes. The din was terrible, but over it the young lady screamed, "We're married, Elmer. Hank quit his job and we went out to Weaverville and got married!"

"Yessir," Hank yelled over the racket. "I told the Forest Service to shove it and took that bus run up out of Crescent City!"

"S'pose you're headed for the fanciest hotel in Eureka fur your honeymoon!" Elmer's wife howled as she surged through the door. "Oh, I so hope you two make a go of it. Ya ain't neither one of ya been married before, have ya?"

"We're green at it all right," Hank bellowed back, "but we'll make out!"

They squalled on about how Ma was dead set against it but Pa said, "Ya can't have her tied to your apron strings forever —that is, when she's not milking our thirteen cows."

"Well, I suppose you're heading out and want to be on your way," hollered Elmer. "Come and see us after the honeymoon's over!"

"Couldn't've stopped to gab tonight," roared Hank, "but there's a big slide over the road two miles downriver. We almost run the Hup into it, and more came down while we was backin' away!" As he yelled "away!" the pump stopped and the word hung ludicrously in the quiet air. Then, as if tiptoeing along a precipice, he said softly, "We figgered to stay here tonight. We know you ain't set for tourists yet, but all we need is some covers and we'll sleep on the floor."

"No need to," Elmer grinned. Joy and force appeared on his face, for he was about to use what he felt was an impressive phrase. "It just so happens," he said, "it just so happens I got a extra room with a bed in the second story."

So they stayed. They made a good couple. He was a large man with light hair and white eyelashes and a kind of cocky clumsiness. I guessed his age at twenty-five and the girl around twenty-one. Not that it meant much; it could have been the other way around. Still, my averages are pretty good. The girl was all bust and bottom with a minimum of waist to tie them together and rather heavy legs, through her ankles were trim and well-proportioned. She was a honey. I saw all that in the dim light and my staring was evidently obvious, for the groom began to glare at me. I noticed it at once and resolutely worked my way into a confab with the old timers about possible quartz faults up in the Muletail Basin of the Pell.

Elmer and his wife took the newlyweds into the restaurant part, where they gossiped, drank coffee, and played old popular records on an ornate and battered Victrola. An hour later one of the prospectors went to the door and, peeking out, reported that the weather had changed. We all went out on the porch and found the air balmy. It was a Chinook wind brushing through and tomorrow would be fair, they foretold. Even as we stood talking, warmer drafts wafted by and thick mists began to build up, through which the warm, steady rain fell.

When we were once again inside, I felt I had acquired enough knowledge and stood up to take my leave and make a camp across the river, for they said there was a bridge a half mile below. I got my pack and started to leave, but Elmer would have none of it.

"Look here," he said, "two bits will buy you a dry room for the night. Why, a night like this is hard on fish."

Two bits, I measured to myself. With two bits worth of flour, coffee, and beans I could live for three days, if I could latch onto a rabbit or a couple of trout.

"Thanks," I answered, "and thanks for the ride, but a quarter will buy two pounds of bacon. I'll get along and find an old shed and hole up till morning."

"They ain't no old shed for miles. Come on, just give me fifteen cents. I've got a lot of overhead and I need some more nails."

"Wish I could, but I'll amble along and find a big stump, get my back against it and my tent wrapped around me. I'll be all right."

He grumbled something and I got my pack on and headed out, but he overhauled me out in the rain. "Look, fella," he growled low, as if the darkness might tattle about his lack of successful commercialism, "I'm gonna put you in an unfinished room up in the second story. Nothin's in there but a pile a secondhand bureaus. You'll have to lay on the floor, but you got your sleeping bag. Just be hellishen quiet so the others don't get wind of me handing out a room for nothin'."

As he said this he led me around the looming jumble of his building and shoved me up the first few steps of some stairs by which his patrons climbed to the sleeping rooms above. The stairs of new, rough lumber creaked and the rusty, reclaimed hinges of the outer door and my room door squawked to wake the dead, but the rich sentimentality of John McCormick singing *Memories* (pronounced "mammaries") against the orchestra and scratches on the record definitely hid from his guests the fact that at Elmer's Inn rooms could be had for free.

With the stub of a candle out of my pack and lit, I beheld myself in canted mirrors of the bureaus. When at last the big down sleeping bag was around me, I fell asleep with no preliminaries.

Later I was awakened by the rasping screech of secondhand hinges and heard one of the old prospectors go limping to his room down the hall. The walls between the rooms were made of coarse, wide boards without battens at the cracks. I heard him sigh some three rooms away from me. The springs of his bed complained shrilly.

Again I dozed, only to be jerked awake once more by the unnerving scream of the rusty hinges as the two other prospectors hobbled their way to rooms across the hall.

We all lay in our board boxes of rooms and listened for awhile to a vaudevillian delivery of *Swanee River* downstairs. Harry Lauder personalized some old favorites to pieces, and then it was back to John McCormick, who was all choked up about something that had happened in the early morning hours —"At Dawning," he said. Evidently it prompted the young couple to become aware of some unfinished business, for shortly after they came up through the heralding of door and stairs, lit a lamp in the room next to mine, and took residence by unpacking a valise and hanging clothing on nails Elmer had hammered into the walls.

Just then I got a bit of down that had worked through my sleeping bag into my throat. At first I knew I would sneeze, but pressing my finger hard against my lip under my nose averted that. Then, the down tickling unmercifully, I felt nothing could stop me from coughing, but I steeled myself and lay in a cold sweat until I finally swallowed the feather. But after that I couldn't relax, and lay distraught and fidgety. So I thought of Virgin Creek and tried to picture the spot where I'd find the first hint of rich deposit.

Inside their room, from which light teased through the cracks, they were still hanging stuff up and taking it down and hanging it somewhere else—or so it sounded. Probably stricken dumb by the momentousness of the hour. The groom took off his shoes and padded about over the creaky floor, then the girl stepped out of her pumps and the tapping of highheels was gone. The groom took off his pants; I heard the cash in his pockets clink against the wall as he hung them on a nail. With straining ears I heard softer sounds as other clothing fell— feminine clothing, I was sure—and then the man who had told the Forest Service to "shove it" said "Gosh!" reverently. After a moment he padded over and turned the lamp up much higher, for the cracks in the wall became bright, narrow ribbons. Finally he said "Wow!" low and with fervor, and one of them blew out the lamp.

He must have found her in the dark, but they tripped on some clothing, I guess, and fell in their embrace against the wall between us. You could hear the crash through the whole structure. It shook my room, but evidently they didn't hear it, for they kissed and kept murmuring over each other, leaning and rolling against the bulging, squeaking wall. Their bed was more articulate than all the rest of the rackety house, and on it they flung themselves and learned how to be one, as the preacher said, and practiced until they were A-one at it, and by that time it must have been three o'clock.

After the sounds of consummation, the quiet of the night was poetry. Again I heard the river, the soft drip of the eaves, and was drifting off again with some odd phrase of McCormick's high, unctious singing repeating itself in my head, now cleansed by drowsiness, when a sense of nausea brushed through me, followed shortly by tremendous gurglings and rumblings in that section between my diaphragm and the seat of my pants. I lay still, flat on my back, while more queasiness came, accompanied by rumblings symphonic and portentious. Then suddenly I was awake and stricken aware of what the score was and as quickly as possible got my coat on but didn't have time for pants and, barefoot, stole over the floor.

My door made one sick squawk and was still, the hall floor crackled under my feet, and the outside door complained with a rusty shriek that must have had every sleeper in the house bolt upright. I hadn't opened it wide enough to get through and started opening it farther, again slowly. That was worse. I slowed it until it barely moved, but it sounded like some hag witch under torture on the rack, so I flung it wide and rushed down the stairs and, in the dark yard, hunted feverishly for the privy until, realizing that every second was precious, I quit hunting.

Afterward, going back, I found I'd overshot the privy by fifty feet. Terribly embarrassed at the racket I'd made, I was certain that all his guests now knew that Elmer's room could be had without the jingle of quarters or even pennies. My return was impressive. Everywhere I stepped boards creaked and popped, and the door emitted sounds unnameable, but I finally got bedded down and asleep. I was in a dream of gold that got blacker and blacker as I hoarded it, and the hoard got bigger and about burst its iron-bound box. I awoke, jumped to my feet, sprinted to the hall, battered open the door, and fell down the stairs, but I still made the privy unhurt and in time.

As I was coming back, the door again burst open and the big prospector rushed by me in his underwear, and when I was once more back in my bag I heard the groom trying to get out of their room without waking his bride, and then I rushed down again and the other prospectors did too. For an hour or so that creaking, noisy place resounded to our hurried feet. I got so I could recognize each man's trot as I passed them in the deep gloom of the rainy night. Shortly after the bride started trotting from bed to backyard, I became dead to the world and was wondrously empty.

When I awoke, the house was still. Quietly I crammed my things into the packboard bag, then sneaked to the door. Elmer had oiled the hinges. It was late morning, but I felt sure that everyone but me was still asleep, recovering from whatever was wrong with last night's meal.

I left that still, rough-board structure and headed downriver to the bridge and, crossing, lazed weakly along the sunlit trail until I found a place where a brook passed through an area of small, busy firs. There I set up my tent and hardly had I done so when a shower came, making everything glisten with its clinging drops in the sun. I cut fir boughs, snapped them dry, put my bed cloth of waterproof canvas on them, flung my bag on top and, crawling in, knew nothing until late afternoon.

I awoke rested and hungry. There must have been lots of sun and wind while I slept, for the ground was quite dry. It seemed like an early spring day. With twigs and little pitchy branches from the firs, I made a fire close before my tent—a shed-like affair opened wide at the front to receive and reflect the fire's heat. It was soon so warm I pulled off my coat. Fried bacon and hotcakes and three eggs carried this far from home wrapped in newspaper were my meal, and with my first pot of beans on the coals rolled and lit a Bull Durham cigarette and enjoyed its fragrance mingled with that of the campfire.

A kind of serenity came over me such as I hadn't known since childhood. It filled me with wonder, and yet I didn't want to express it. It was mine here and now to be lived, not to be conveyed. Creature comfort? Oh, much more than that. A wondrousness, a marvel, permeating the rocks and the sky just as I was immersed in it. No melody from our music titillated my mind, no thoughts of grandeur of race, no hopes or philosophical summations. I didn't rest or aspire. All I knew was a serene sense of being, of being alive and a part of the world, a part of the little trees and the fire's crackling and of the rocks about. All I knew seemed a delicate configuration of the very bounds of knowing and of matter, touching many opposed theories as truth showed all the great enigmas to be true answers, the unanswers of the outside world.

The old man grasped my shoulder. "I've got it figured you ain't asleep," he said. "Glen and Max are dead to the world. What you thinking?"

I heard once more the racket of our traveling. His question was casual enough, but I decided to go with my instincts.

"I've come to it that you, same as me, figure life is also a mental adventure," I said. He didn't answer, but I sensed that he was with me, so I went on in all my naiveté. "It is to me, at least," I said, "but more than just intellectual. It's a physical and emotional adventure too, and when you join the three you

67

come on things hard to put words to. Could it be that all the hogwash of religions is based on different men's interpretations of certain experiences that kindle all of us one time or another?"

"Self-befuddlement?" he said.

"You think so?"

"Uh, uh," he answered. "Oh, I'll venture ninety percent of these personal phenomena, these sensings, the brief glances down vaguely comprehended vistas are cluttered with self-deceit to a point to make all staid folk turn away, and yet—"

"Yeah, and yet!" I insisted eagerly. "Why don't you turn away from them? It's easier!"

He went right on: "Once you've peered down one of these holes in the wall, you can't range again with the denouncers of religion, anymore'n you can stand the pap and conduct of religions or those who espouse them."

"That shoe fits me," I said. "Maybe we're both three-toed sloths."

"Shut up," he said. "Ideas are for the cubbyholing of our necessity. Our very tool of thought, our logic and our need to make everything taut and simple, stops us from ever coming to grips with actuality. But in spite of self-befuddlement I think the most honest of us have glimpses that make the stable laws of hedonists and metaphysicians alike seem matters of conceit."

"But," I said, overwhelmed by his outburst, "—but if simplification is necessary to us as men, isn't this battering through to the place where this tool of constriction is, without edge, an idiot's occupation?"

"My guess," said the old man, "is that some arboreal nonconformist ages back tried walking on the ground between groves and extended his range, and in time his relatives followed. The other end of the rope of that tendency—who knows? It's in the future. We sports of this domestic breed are really thankless bellwethers. You and I will probably die as laughing stocks of the steers, the cattle people, but one in a thousand of us fastens onto a shift that's right for the moment and goes down in history as a prime mover."

"What good?"

"Reward and the reason why out of it. See it as it is. We impractical, vague ones are the only ones who stumble onto the next larger pattern. Another strange thing is that the cattle people, though they bellow before they accept the patterns, follow. You wouldn't think they would. It's really a mad, cosmic trick on them, but they follow."

"You call them the cattle people," I responded. "I call them the Smiths and the Joneses. They're always imitating each other. The women lead in this department. Sometimes it's oak furniture; they give up their mahogany and save for oak. Or Van Dyke beards. They gotta get what the other guy's gettin' —the urge is in their blood. They don't know deep-down why, and the usual explanations miss the point. What's really so is that the Smiths and the Joneses are at the very core of human-ity, and in our great passage down through time their constant involvement and imitation of the other fellow's actions, his moods and modes, stabilizes the core of mankind as we move through time, while we sports, several layers from the core, stumble and dance ever' which way to test the weather and the road ahead."

There was a pause, and then he turned his face towards me in the darkness. I could feel his breath on my cheek. "Christ! I never seen it that way," he said, "but you could be right. One thing's for sure, though: the cattle people—your Smiths and Joneses—snub our kind. We don't belong—no elk tooth fob, no ribbon, button, speech mannerism or straight jacket to accredit us."

"Hell, man, you don't talk like a sheriff."

"Sure, Willie, and I accused you of being cockeyed to your front. Okay, so we both are." Then he added, by way of afterthought: "Say, give it to me straight. Are you a fruit?"

"On the contrary," I answered, "I'm a tit man myself, a fondler of women. But you're not the first to ask me that. It makes me sore. There's no lily about me. You one of those nice clean old men?"

"I was married to Mrs. Kindrid for forty-one years," he said. "The only thing I share with the homo is the knowledge of being outside the pale with the criminal and the whore."

"Okay," I said, "okay."

"Tell me," he said, "I'm curious: why did you go prospecting in the winter?"

"It was then or never. You tell me why you're riding this freight?"

He didn't answer for a long moment, and when he did it lacked his usual power. "I don't know. In a way I do. I could make a diagram, but it wouldn't cover much of the ground. Oh, it ain't so much," he went on, "but as I study it sometimes I get confused. Maybe I'm in my dotage, or maybe—hell!" he said, "I just don't know. I told you I was a sheriff. In a lot of ways I was built for it, except for one part of me. Tell you, I never brought a man in or turned him loose or shot him and stood over him in the dust, but as I stared I saw him as he was as a baby. This little part of me could wipe away the years, the erosions of misadventure, and see him as a toddler and from the toddler read back through the guessed years till he was once more the man. And guessing the whys of it, compassion 'ud choke me—me the instructed hand of the law, cast-iron with one kind of honesty while that other honesty watched nonplussed and ashamed of its residence in me."

"Have you really killed men?"

"Was my job—my contract with the community. I jailed 'em, I clubbed 'em, and I shot 'em, but I was just, according to the law."

"Why didn't you quit and take up different work?"

"As long as I believed in law and its measly attempts at real justice, I couldn't dodge that I was better fitted than most to deal out its harshness."

"Why?"

"Because even when I was a kid I realized the need for law. What I did was something needed where I was."

"Don't some of the things you did haunt you?"

"Some. More if I'd let 'em. But the law is the best we got as yet. I don't like it anymore, but I wouldn't set it aside. I ain't against it. Law has got once removed from man and taken on a cold life of its own. Someday we'll put compassion and humor into it and stop all unnecessary coldness. I'll be dead then. That's the way I ended my third term—quit being the county's robot, and they said I got soft. I was learning a lot all the time, reading every chance I got—yeah, and mulling it all over—and just when I got so I was really understanding men and their shortcomings I was old and out of office." He was silent long enough for me to become aware of the noise and jar of the train. And then he said, "The transients and vags played hob with me more than most."

I wondered about his last remark as we slowed and rolled into a siding. When the whole train was clear of the main track, it stopped. We jumped down and relieved ourselves. We were away from the river in what looked like cutover stump country with brush hiding even those evidences that the land was once clothed with timber. The moon rode low in the west, storm clouds were gone, and stars were part of the quietness of the hour.

The old man got out a corncob pipe, stuffed it from a bag of beechnut tobacco and lit it. No flower ever produced such ecstasy in my nose as I stood in his smoke's drift. I'd been without tobacco for six days.

"Give me a few flakes of that, will you?" I asked. He reached into his coat pocket, brought it out and handed it to me and I stuffed some flakes into a tiny pipe made of an acorn that I had been smoking since my hands got too stiff to roll a cigarette from panning in the Pell.

"Thanks," I said.

We puffed away standing on the rails, balancing on them as a fellow does around tracks.

"You going all the way to Tiburon?" I asked.

He said he was, but didn't seem to want to talk. Glen and Max had gone back into our cave, but others stood out on the tracks. There must have been a dozen of us riding through. We waited, the whole train waited. Finally it seemed to me that time and volition were no more. The train and the tracks and we bums, standing here and there in the dark, and the thickets beside the tracks—all seemed part of a pointless tableau, a meaningless summation, a dream dreamt in the grave. We were caught up in silence, and silence was a world of its own. Then through it I heard far down the tracks, miles down the tracks, a faint wail from the engine of an oncoming train.

With faces lifted to the sound we gazed into the darkness and waited. We opened our mouths and swung our heads, trying one ear and then the other, and eventually we heard it again, though this time much fainter.

The old man said there were hills between us now. "Blew the first time when it passed a notch. These train men 'uv got angles to their trade; knowing where the land will carry their signals best is one of them. In Tennessee there's a famous spot where they hoot their approach."

"Have you covered much ground on freights?" I asked.

"Most all states," he answered, knocking out his pipe on the rail. "Missed Maine and Wyoming. Wyoming's my home state. Don't feel a former officeholder should bum in his own state."

Our locomotive screamed into the night. After a long, breathless wait we took the answering wail—louder now—into our mouths and ears, and the approaching of it sped our heartbeats. We stood as if exultant, holding our senses, our full stature from the ground, but the sounds of its approach came to us instead through our feet. The rails set up a vague vibration and while we stooped to touch them with our hands the locomotive rounded the final hill. Its distant panting sounded brave and indomitable.

We crawled into our haven but stayed at the opening, peering out. The locomotives called to each other savagely, hauntingly. Ours was strident. "Steel bound, steel bound," it screamed. And toiling nearer through the tangled country, that other moaned, "Almost souls, almost have souls, souls, souls." It came into the straightaway and roared past our engine and charged by us with its long black belly full of fire and its demonic eye glittering on the rails before it. Its many sliding, gliding, clanking parts chattered, "Steam 'n' steel, steam 'n' steel, steam 'n' steel," and it was past, and the long string of dark boxcars that it was dragging behind it clattered by us. Then slowly we started moving again and it was gone. Its caboose passed us with a brakeman easy on its steps, and we were alone, clear to proceed. And over their shoulders the locomotives called to each other once more before the coils and defiles of the land were able to swallow such messages.

As we gained speed the side drafts began to chill us and we got back to our old places and arranged the tent about us and over our heads.

"What's this tent weigh?" said the old man.

"Three pounds four ounces," I answered. "My wife sewed it up out of light muslin, and I waterproofed it. She made the sleeping bag too, and my canvas coat."

"Some wife," said Max to the old man. "Let's have a pull on my bottle. You know," he went on, "if I could find me a broad like that I'd take her home to Walla Walla, marry her there, and settle down and help out at the store. Could get a game going nights for real moola."

We had our drink, swaying along drowsily. After that wait, slamming ahead seemed a luxury we had done without for awhile.

"Really movin'," said Glen. "How far do you think we've come?"

"I'd say we're north of Willits about thirty miles," answered Max. "Been along her lots of times in my Buick."

"Won't be long 'fore it lightens," mumbled the old man from his beard.

I thought I'd answer, but found nothing to say and no power to say it. We were all caught in the low ebbing of life before dawn. The boy sighed. Getting homesick, I surmised. I was too dull to talk him out of it. God, I was dull! And yet my thoughts left the shell of my dullness easily. It was thinking of a strange kind—not willful daydreaming, but a subconscious dreaming while just very drowsy.

First it was pictures, faded as old postcards found half-burned and sodden amid the debris of a rubbish fire—pictures of Eureka streets, the railroad station, and the dairy farms on the flat about. I drowsed along, staring inwardly, and then wondered if it was getting light. I stuck my head out from the tent and stared from our tunnel toward the east. There wasn't even a trace of light yet.

Back in my place I gave myself up to daydreaming. Willfully I put myself back in the little camp by the brook after the night spent at Elmer's. I would remember that day clearly, and so bridge to the time when there'd be light in the eastern sky, for now I longed for it. This night had gone on for centuries, it seemed, and I wanted to be done with it. But in daydreaming I couldn't see my camp, but only how pale, how very pale, the first signs of dawn coming would be on the horizon and how, as you pondered this extreme vagueness, it changed quality somehow and established a certain hue in the light. And then it reached up from the horizon a bit and faded some stars, and as you observed this you saw that it had reached north and south and had outlined the mountains clearly. And then the hue was different, though you could really find no change, and other stars were gone and about you trees and barns, old fence posts and hills, shone faintly on the sides that faced east. And on came the light and the faint hue became color and then the whole sky was lighter and the colors were joyous while night slid away to the west and cloaked the Pacific. And the birds and cattle and lone horses standing silent in night pastures turned their heads and drew life from the burning east.

74

I had to look out again. It wouldn't bother the others. They sat as if doped while I pulled back the tent. Still dark! Hell! I settled back in my place and remembered that the first day in from the road. I remembered that I camped all day and that night amongst those little, busy firs, and left next morning before sunup with my kit packed carefully in the packboard bag, light stuff in the bottom, heavy stuff high by my shoulders and close to the boards so it wouldn't pry on the shoulder straps—eighty pounds of duffel arranged just right. I sat it on a log to get it on. Mustn't swing it on and off today; forty of those took energy, and the three thousand foot climb on the twelve mile hike that was ahead of me would sap all the energy I owned.

THE TRAIL TURNED ABRUPTLY from the flat and zigzagged up the face of the bluff-like end of the ridge that lay between the basin of the Pell and the Chiltaw River drainage. I took the first steep pitches of the trail with little, slow steps, leaning carefully forward for just the right balance, and I kept my heart and mind almost sleepy with calm. The gray light was much too slight to show the dew on the grass beside the trail, and then I was up in the rocks shifting to another swing of the zigzag. Those little, easy steps didn't make me puff. I looked about, feeling like a turtle under my load, plodding along under it but being able to swivel my head around as if it were apart from the striving. At the top of the sixth zigzag I eased the pack to rest on a rock and slipped loose of it. Without its weight I felt toppily, as if my feet didn't touch the ground. Then I made myself floppy, swaying myself, loosening up before resting. But I only half-rested and then slipped the pack on and started up again. By noon I was over half way, according to my map, and a little taut but not tired.

Coming in from Eureka the road had climbed, but now it was up, up, and more up. After lunch and a long rest and smoke, I started again, lamely at first but soon sweating into it. I got easy for awhile, but soon grew quite tired. The load was lead on my back, the shoulder straps implacable iron bands. I began putting force and will into it, though I allowed myself to do no more than trudge. Not a stride did I take that day. I trudged and trudged, always climbing. The hours crawled by and I was weary and the winter sun was weary and low in the cloudy southwestern sky. I tottered on and topped the ridge as the sun touched the horizon in a flurry of clouds. I came up around a bank of rock and through a crooked saddle and beheld the snow-capped mountains where I was going. They stood remotely, like sentinels, up at the back of the great cupped palm that is the Muletail Basin of the Pell.

I took out my map and shivered. Yes, the map showed them to be Hoss Mountain, Snider's Peak, and the Chiltaw Buttes. They reared up their snow-covered rocks high above the timberline, painted gaudy by the setting sun, yet cold against a dark bank of clouds to the north. I shivered again. Would I be able to truck through the great basin and climb the mountains that rimmed it, find my way through the rotten snow and water traps of Tetno Pass, and come safely with my load down to that valley where years before a man's mine had just disappeared? The owner, after carrying out his pokes for safe keeping, had not been able to find it when he got back, had hunted high and low for years and never found it. And yet I was sure I would be able to. I'd just walk, listening—ah, listening very carefully —and find it.

Such was the dream that brought me into this country, but that was before I saw Virgin Creek on the map and knew at once I should first go there. I turned from the view and found a flat area that topped the ridge. It was too late to go farther. I laid down my pack and, loosening the axe from it, climbed the one small branchy fir about and, working down it, cut off all its bushy limbs. I saw I'd have to hump for all I was worth to make a snug camp before dark, for now clouds from north and from southwest were blanketing most of the sky, and high above me herds of little sheep clouds were being obscured by lower stuff moving the other way.

I was on a peak, I realized, in changing weather in the winter, and might be snowed in. While I pondered, the wind changed and blew strongly from a different direction and then changed again.

"Now, by God," I said aloud, "I've got to make ready for anything, and fast!" I dragged the boughs near to the camp spot and began gathering fuel. If it snowed deep I'd get damn little wood from the great trunks of the firs about. First I went far out and dragged large fallen limbs in until I was about one hundred feet from camp. I'd drop them there and go back for more. When darkness was complete I had a ring of large limbs around the camp. Then I went in and built a fire and put up my tent and dragged the boughs in, and by the light of the fire I brought in that perimeter of fuel until it was in a semi-circle closed around the fire with my tent plugging the gap. I believe I had enough fuel for a week or more, and there was grub enough in my pack to hold me over ten days in a pinch.

Having achieved some semblance of order, I built my bough bed carefully and laid my things beside it in the tent. The pot of beans was bubbling on the coals and a big biscuit of dough god was rising in the frying pan, but there was only water enough in my little canteen to moisten dough for the biscuit. There was none to drink, and there had been no sign of water for the last five miles on the trail.

Thirst prodded me to think about it as I arranged the camp and cut enough wood for the night. I fluffed my down bag on the boughs and secured the tent every way I could for the wind and, growing thirstier all the time, I at last hit upon the way to get water.

I hadn't yet learned that you can run with a candle in a coffee can. That simple backwoods lantern was several days away from being part of my resources, and a flashlight was too heavy to carry where an ounce weighs a pound by noon and five pounds by night. One thing I had to have was a big bonfire, so I made one well out from the tent. I got the dough god out of the fryingpan and filled the pan with new coals and twigs. Then I grabbed my pail and ran down the trail as it proceeded into the basin, for I'd seen a ravine along it as I stared at the mountains, and in that ravine there might be water.

In the wind of running, the coals and twigs glowed and burned, and though they barely allowed me to see the trail, I rushed headlong down it and within a quarter of a mile came upon a spring. Dipping out a pailful, I rushed back, but the coals glowed dimly and the trail ran among cliffs. Still, with legs ready to give out, I scurried on faster until the coals ceased to glow at all. I waited then in the dark until finally I could see a faint illumination from my bonfire and, stumbling about among the boles of trees, I climbed the rough ground below camp and soon was sitting down to my dinner with such a sense of foolhardy accomplishment that I laughed aloud.

The peak was soon the rendezvous of strong winds from several directions. I finally had to throw dirt on my fire and bank it in, for gusts blew coals into the tent. How the tent stayed up under the pressure was a marvel to me.

Though dog-tired, I slept but fitfully, concerned and yet strangely happy at the wild sough of the wind-tossed pines. I lay wishing for more powerful gusts and then, when I heard them approaching, hoping they would not blow my tent over and wondering when the next storm would hit. Next morning the sun shining through the wall of my tent woke me. I stared up at the trees, warm in the sunlight, then I rolled over and looked at the awkward bulwark of dead limbs piled around the fire and tent. It was hard to believe I'd amassed it in so short a time. A little scared perhaps? Well, maybe.

That night in the very last of twilight I reached Emby. A faint drizzle had been coming down for several hours, and the lit windows in the log cabin aroused my herd instinct. A hound bayed, for a night draft was at my back and bore my scent before me. He came floundering up the trail, but once to me and spoken to, he licked my hand and kept banging in friendliness against my legs as I moved down to the store, a two-story log cabin with an outside stairway. By the door of the store several bearded men sat on a bench under the overhang of the roof and fed chips to the little fire before them. Through a window I could see rows of canned beans and milk on a shelf in the store. So I said "Evening" to the men and opened the door, which rang a little bell. A tall, broad-shouldered woman who was seated beside the stove mending an extremely holey sock looked up over her glasses at me, saw I was a stranger, and leaped to her feet. The leap flung her glasses off, but she caught them in mid-air.

"Thay," she started to say, then hurried behind the counter where she ducked and came up with a mouthful of teeth— "S-say," she said, "you put a scare in me being a stranger'n all. That pack's a funny contraption for sure."

"It handles pretty good," I answered. "Had some theories on carrying a load and worked them out in this rig. Came up to do a little mining."

She grinned compassionately: "Prospectors 'n' miners is all we got around here. Husband 'n' I came up for gold years ago 'n' decided to settle for silver and pennies. Wolf ain't been too near the door sence."

The store had the bare necessities of food and clothing through which hardware was strewn as if, combined, it completed the tale of a loner's existence. Bars of yellow naphtha soap stood on the shelf in the box they came in. There looked to be about seven different brands of chewing tobacco in a glass case with fishhooks and ammunition. Rolled oats, kidney beans, and prunes stood about in gunnysacks with the tops rolled down like turtleneck sweaters. There were wedges, sledge hammers, mattocks, and shovels, and a few patent medicines. Sides of bacon were hung from the ceiling throughout the place, except where a little chickenwire cage with small counter and wicket was jammed against the wall along with a display of leather trusses, long red underwear, and three assorted horse collars. The woman told me it was the post office.

"Those eggs fresh?" I asked of a basketful on the counter.

"That's right," she answered. "Our own chickens. Black Minorcas is what they are. Don't lay so heavy, but the yolks has got what you need. They's fine poached, but so's doe meat. Barren does is the best poached meat there is." She snickered over this and continued snickering about it as I said I'd take a dozen and a wedge.

I had an idea about bedrock mining. I couldn't pack in a sledge hammer to slug it with, but I was sure going to pack in a big steel wedge.

She wrapped them up. "They'll go good together," she allowed, "—that is, if you got the mustard."

"Oh, I have," I said and looked innocently at her, at which she burst out laughing.

"Perhaps," she said, "perhaps," still laughing. "Couldn't get this far without a little. You goin' up river?"

"Yes, and when I get located I'll be down for a packload of grub."

"Better bed down in the woodshed then and have breakfast with us. It'll only set you back twenty cents."

I agreed, feeling I was just throwing money around. But then I was here, wasn't I, up where I could pile up a fortune? We'll live up here, Nordi and Bunky and I, in a great log chalet with hardwood floors.

"What you standing there dreaming about?" the woman wanted to know. It flustered me.

"I was considering a few more purchases," I blustered out prissily. Christ, I thought. I spit, feeling my mouth was contaminated. She noticed it.

"Maybe you'd like a plug of Kentucky Fine Leaf," she said.

"Yeah, wrap it up."

"Take it as it is," she said. "Paper's hard to come by this far back."

I took the plug. She was watching me narrowly. I don't know why, but somehow I felt I had to take a big chew even though I'd never had tobacco in my mouth before. I thought of cutting off a morsel but still I felt that wouldn't be satisfactory to the woman, who I was sure was taking my measure—and not for herself alone, but also for the mountains and their denizens who regarded plug tobacco so high that she, their judge and agent, must stock seven different brands. No sir, for this trial I must certainly chomp off a mighty quid. So, opening my mouth wide, I bit down on it to sink my teeth through its toughish munchiness—or so I had always assumed it to be. But I could have bit through one of those horse collars with more ease. Pulling, grinding away, I saw she still had her sharp eyes on nothing but me. I took the plug out of my mouth.

"Gimme three pounds of beans and a pound of lean bacon," I said. A third of the plug shone with my saliva where I had gnawed at it and my teeth marks were in a semi-circle, indicating clearly what I thought was a man-sized chew. I put it back in my mouth and fitted my teeth into the holes and ground away again.

"You don't want lean bacon," the woman said, "you want all the fat you can get to fry with. Deer meat is powerful dry without some bacon fat to help her slide when you swallow."

She waited my word, leaning out over her counter and staring at me. I took the glistening plug from my mouth. "Make it fat," I said, then put the plug back, got fitted to it, and bit down till my eyes bulged. The woman had not moved from her leaning stance out over her counter, only now she had a paring knife in her hand for me. But I shook my head and ground away, feeling that now my life depended on it, and finally severed my chunk from the plug, which I stowed in my pocket while I tried to get the huge morsel into my cheek. It was too big for that. Hot tobacco juice was burning my mouth and tonsils and running down my throat, and my stimulated saliva glands were gushing, but the quid was in the way so I swallowed. More came at once—tobacco juice was just running out of that quid. The woman saw I was in trouble.

"Here," she said, "spit in the stove." She rushed around her counter and flung its door open. I reached in my mouth and removed the thing to spit and then afterwards started to put it back.

"Throw the filthy thing in the fire," the woman said beside me. "Go on. You're no chewer and what of it. It's a dirty habit."

I tossed that wallered quid into the flames. "Just thought I'd try," I murmured.

"Sure," she answered warmly, "did myself once." And she turned her back and started weighing the beans while I wandered out into the darkness. I was beginning to be a pretty sick prospector.

Next morning after breakfast I started up the trail only thirty miles or so from my goal. I was now packing ninety-two pounds by the store's scales, with the wedge accounting for eight. I pushed along for several miles through a cedar flat. Its floor was mulch from which the giant trunks soared; the needles and twigs of centuries had covered the muck, and walking on it was a pleasant, springy business, but my boots started to wear at me at the back just above the heel.

A mile further I took them off. Sixteen inch Oil Kings they were, hobbed with the sharp cones of Hungarian nails. The trouble was I'd stood them wet by the stove in the store where the woman's husband had told me to. I'd stood them with their backs to the heat and a little too close, for now their backstraps were shrunken and rubbed on my Achilles tendons, which were extremely painful.

Little things like this can turn men from their quests, I said to myself, but not me. No sir, I'll back up the hills if necessary. Maybe tonight I can make a rig to pry them into their old shape.

And so I trudged along the trail, groaning when I inadvertently touched the sore spots. At any steep pitches I turned around and slowly backed up. After a mile or so of this

I backed up a steep ascent where the trail left the Pell and traveled an area of roly-poly hills, hardly more than mounds. I would hurry down one side and turn around and back up the other, trying to make time and still not hit trees or fall down. I grew very weary. Half way up one I was backing away stubbornly when I was astounded to see a body on each side of the trail where I had just passed, and in such attitudes as if they had been thrown there. Then I saw their eyes. No crime had been committed; they were alive.

"Hello," I said, feeling very foolish. What must they think of me backing into the gold country. Now they were grinning at me and getting to their feet.

"Ef ya got reasons for comin' up here thataway," said the older of the two, "we uns 'ud sutainly lak to know."

Though their talk wasn't all that understandable, I did know who they were, for they'd sprawled in such abandon as only hounds and hookworm southerners can affect.

"My boots are pinching the tendons above my heels."

"Ef such happened to me a'da holed up right thar till they 'uz better," he said, looking me sharply up and down, "or trade 'em for gear what didn't bind me."

"Gon' t'eat when the stew gets hot. Will you set with us?" asked the boy.

"Thanks, but I've got to get on."

"Aw, you ain't in such a hurry, air ye?" asked the older man. "We'd sure lak for ya to set with us and spend the day."

"It would be a pleasure," I said, "but I've been five days getting this far."

"And still got twenty-five miles to go," he answered, grinning at me. The boy grinned too.

"More or less," I agreed, looking them over. They were lank and slow, with lantern jaws and immense hands and feet. The man had squatted down in the path and was following an ant's course with a twig. Finally he spit on it and the ant gave up to Lady Nicotine, or probably drowned before the poison got on its awful work.

85

"Just where you figgerin' on doin' your diggin'?"

"Oh," I answered, "gold's where ya find it, they say. I'll peck around as I go till I find a likely spot."

"On the main river?"

"Or its tributaries," I said, feeling indulgent toward these transplanted hillbillies.

"Lak Virgin Crick?" pursued the man.

"Or any other creek," I said.

"Name 'em," he demanded, though still smiling and friendly.

Hell, I hadn't paid attention to the names of the others. "Well, there's Virgin Creek and—the East Fork," I said.

"Friend," he answered, "they ain't no East Fork. What'd be is called Kelsey Crick, and you're headin' fir Virgin Crick, ain't ya?"

"I'm goin' where I'm goin'," I answered, fury boiling up in me at last. "What makes ya so goddamned curious?"

"Look, friend," he said, "cam down. We uns ain't laffin' at you alone, but at all of us fellas what's come up here. All of us to a man headin' sure of our signs for Virgin Crick. Why, a passel of Chinks picked that cherry seventy years ago, and the likes of you and me been worryin' around in the Virgin's bed ever since. That damned crick shoulda been named Old Whore Crick a long time ago, cuz it 'ud saved every newcomer to these mountains a lot of shoe leather and what not."

I stood before him a ruined man while the boy helped me off with my pack.

"Lordy, Tom," he said, "look what this puny-wristed fella has been humpin' uphill and bassakwards."

Tom hefted it. "Thing lak that could sap your strength. Ever'thin' but the kitchen sink, uh?" His smile was kindly on me, for he knew I was suffering a complicated sorrow.

"Just about," I admitted forlornly. "Say, I don't know how I'm gonna thank you two."

"Firgit it," the man said.

"Yea, firgit it," the boy said after him. And we started toward the stew.

Their shanty was not a stone's throw away, but obscured by bushy cedars. Some barnacled bastard had built it like a ship's cabin, the bunks narrow against the wall and the whole house put together with knees. The roof was flatly rounded like the deck of a boat. It was old. It had three small rooms like staterooms on a vessel, and the front room was built with heavy split shakes and calked.

"Fine cabin," I said. "How's you come by it?"

"Jest moved in," they said in chorus.

"They's a dozen cabins up and down the Pell," said Tom. "Ain't nobody in it, hit's yours. Hit's all gonermint land anyhow. They can't be owned, and most of 'em is older than this and lady frail, but they's a cabin up river, couple miles, I hope you take. Us needs a neighbor to confab with."

"I could eat a skunk right now," I announced.

"No need to," answered the boy. "Tom and me tried one last spring. The meat don't stink. It's powerful racy all right, but it ain't got no smell."

The stew they served up was one of the great moments of my life—the epitome of one sort of thing. Proper rottenness in food is a goal sought by people throughout the world. The wonderful taints we used to get from our food are leaving us; we are clean and sterile around our food and the food tastes stark. The old food sometimes killed a lot of people, but not before it paid in advance with moments when the splendid flavors of those hellish taints stood you for a moment with the gods on Mt. Olympus. I once ate, unknowing, of some thoroughly rotten halibut made almost immortal by those exquisite flavors. And once I owned a cheese far older than myself that killed the mice and maggots that sought to eat their way through the filthy crud of its crust. But a silver knife held to its cut face and achieving a microscopic adherence would flavor a proper cracker or biscuit so that, munching it, you were neither here nor there, but part of birth and definitely part of the grave: filth was elegantly yours, and you were ennobled and ravished by the experience. Such was their stew. The bear fat was tainted without being rancid, and the deer meat it greased was shot through with flavors of new life aborning in the corruptions of the old. It was a kind of a death-and-transfiguration stew, I guess. Anyway, I ate an enormous plate of it, quite willing to pay with my life if need be. I lived on, however, as the boy did the dishes. Then we sat in the front room on blocks of wood topped with gunnysacks of straw, and talked and smoked. God how those two smoked: they sucked single-mindedly on their corncob pipes until the coals of tobacco in their pipe bowls glowed like forges, and then, settling back, they put out like human bellows, filling the room with clouds of smoke.

"Now, them shoes," Tom, the older one, said, "them shoes with those back straps'll never get clean back to just where they was. Have you got other footgear among all that stuff you been packin' up here?"

"No," I said sleepily, through billows of smoke. I could only see his great feet clearly.

"They's a fella," he muttered, "come up here las' summer lak you, and he didn't carry out all he brung in. Left me some boots 'bout your size—rubber boots, and never been worn. Too small for Will or me. You could get around in 'em, and I know a fella below Emby needs shoes."

I was so sleepy. I knew he wanted the shoes and I guess it was all right. They were no good to me any longer. Head in the clouds of smoke, I was quite content, and then someone was shaking me.

It was the old man, saying "Wake up! We're in Willits!"

Glen and Max had already gotten out and we followed them out of our hideaway. The sun was up enough to make everything brassy bright after the long hours staring at blackness. Yes, and maybe the peering backwards all night had not accustomed my eyes to the here and now. We stood talking beside the tracks, and then the old man was gone. As I looked about to see where he had gone, Max gritted, "Scatter—here come the yardbulls!"

He took the boy with him under the freightcar and I heard them slamming away from the yards. By that time one of the detectives was close enough to address me. "Hold it! We want to talk to you." I'd gotten my pack and decided to keep it on: where I went it must go.

They came up to me staring boldly. The law was on their side, and from behind it they were safe to prod their oafishness at me.

"Where you from?" one of them said.

"Emby," I told them.

"And where's that?" the smaller man wanted to know.

"Thirty miles north of Waddle."

"Where you going?"

"Home."

"Where's that?"

"Tiburon."

"You know Andrews?" he said, referring to Tiburon's town cop.

"Yes,"

"Describe him to me."

"He's flat on both ends and wears a star in the middle."

"You're a smart guy, uh?"

"If I was I wouldn't be on the bum. I'm just accurate."

"Mouthy, uh?"

I didn't reply. The man's partner was a broad, stupid, division-point railroad bull. He smelled of very stale sweat. His blue serge was protected with leather at the elbows, cuffs, and pockets. It shone with wear and grime. He wore the black hat with a stiff brim much affected by plainclothesmen at the time. The thing that engrossed him more than I did were his shoes. He had on new, broad, black policeman shoes, just like a big city cop. Finally he put them rather far apart with toes straight ahead and, satisfied with his stance of aggressiveness, gave me one of the most blandly wise, implacably brutal-if-need-be looks I had ever seen concocted. But he let his partner do the talking, and grinned as the other fellow went through the trifles.

The other fellow finally gave me a look of compounded slyness. "What if I tell ya—" But he never got to tell me, for the other broke in with "Let me handle this one, Fred."

Fred dawdled about, feeling my pack. The thirty-thirty was against the packboard and he couldn't feel it. "He could be from outta state."

"Andrews is fat," I said, "lots of gold in his teeth, wears a ring. He's left-handed and always salting his beer. Still think I'm out of state?"

"He coulda been outta state."

"I'll handle this now, Fred. You check the rest of the train," said the beefy one. He kept working his feet in the ballast, as if he was getting ready for some mighty effort. I figured he was about to swing a roundhouse of brassknuckles at my chin. Instead he belched—a long, tremendous belch. "Now," he said, "we got reason to believe there's an old man on this train what's wanted, and, you and me both knowin' Andrews, we're sorta friends. Now, we don't know anythin' about this old guy, no description come through yet, but a fella up at Arcata that had had some trouble with him years ago said the old guy come to his place in the night and told him he'd break his neck if he didn't do such and so. They couldn't see him in the dark and him behind a hedge, but the guy said it was him all right. Knew his voice, and anyway he named people and places. But his wife swears the voice she heard wasn't from no old wrinkled guy at all and she thinks—but hell, who cares what she thought, it was him all right and I aim to put the cuffs on him. Now," he said, "did you see an old man about, say, seventy-two on the train? You hop her at Eureka?"

"Yeah, at Eureka," I answered, "but I didn't notice any old man. Lots of fellas forty or fifty, but seventy—hell, he'd a froze. First it rained till we were soaked through and then it froze, and it sleeted most of the night. If he was on last night he probably got off and stayed at the first water tank. They had a big fire there, but I stayed in this hole here. He'd be at the water tank unless another freight passed by now."

"Okay," he said, "you keep this quiet. Don't tell any other cops along the line. No one's got the dope on him but me. I got it from my brother in Omaha by wire last night. Now, you let fall even a hint of this and Andrews and me'll have you behind bars, and them bars'll be the soft part." He gave me a shove that almost toppled me, pack and all. I took it, glad that was all. Where, I wondered, had the old man gone?

Max and Glen came back from hiding. I left my pack with them and followed the cop. He hurried himself along and got into a nondescript car and bored north out of town, heading toward the water tank.

Once more with Max and the boy, I told them the old man was in trouble. "He didn't do nothin'," Glen said at once. "He's been good to us all. You'd be dead," he said to Max, "if it weren't for him, and he helped me all he could."

"They're after him," I said. "When does the freight leave?"

Max said he'd find out and was back shortly. "Fifteen minutes more, and don't go looking around for him. I'll keep the smaller dick from searching the train."

I had an idea. I opened my knife, baring the little razor-sharp blade I kept for slashing rattlesnake bites and opening puncture wounds. Then I went over to a line of cars standing in the yard. The workmen were not about; it was early. I had only the trainmen to watch and, watching my chance, I cut through the metal tape on another sealed car on the siding. I cut it in a manner that allowed the cut place to be behind the hasp of the lock. I could place it on the opened lumber car in such a way that no one would suspect that it was cut. If I could find the old man and stow him in that shifting load, it might be possible to smuggle him down to Tiburon. All night I had been promising myself to cook the smidgen of flour I still carried and gain some strength. I'd eaten a piece of cornbread about noon two days before. I needed food. I hauled my pack over to some bushes near the track and got out that precious

CLYDE RICE

flour—about two teaspoons it was—and, mixing it in a cup with a little ditch water, downed it. My stomach cramped at once, but I held it down until nausea left me.

They shunted the boxcars back and forth for the next half hour, remaking the train. Our car with the protected riding places was shunted onto a spur, and a number of cars were added from a train from Fort Bragg down on the coast. One was an empty gondola—a long, narrow, metal box on wheels, the sides and ends about breast high. When I could not be observed, I skipped out of the brush and placed the filched metal tape with its seal on the hasp of the lumbercar of last night and then, just before the train started, got into the gondola with Max and Glen. There were nine or ten others in it already.

Max was jubilant. "Sold him a railroad watch I picked up in a game on a five-dollar bet. He didn't half search the train, and I got my five back. Seen the old-timer?"

We hadn't. "I believe he's on this train," Max went on. "He's foxy. I listened to him last night, when you and him were spielin'. He's followin' sumpin' in his head, but I'm for him."

Glen nodded. "You bet," he said.

Soon we were on our way, rolling through the foothill country, at last past the canyons of the tributaries of the Eel. There was nothing we could do about the old man. If we chased over the cars hunting, it would only draw notice from the caboose should we find him. The gondola had about an inch of rainwater on the floor, but it was bent up at the forward end from some accident, which produced a space about half as big as a blanket humped up out of the water. All those who could stood there. Latecomers like we three stood in the puddle. I lashed my pack up out of it on the side by tying the shoulder straps that were loose around a rung in the boarding ladder.

The day started as a still, clear morning, but it hazed over slightly as we banged along. The bunch that came up the short line from Fort Bragg stood together on the humped place, had been there all the way up from the coast. When we stopped to

92

pick up a car at Capella, I jumped down and rescued an old tie on the ground beside the track. Max and Glen helped me get it in. After that we stood on it out of the water. There was room for two to stand on, and one could lie down on the tie if he was a good balancer. We took turns, using Glen's little brass-bound kit for a seat or pillow.

"What the hell's the use of going straight anyhow?" Max burst out after a long silence. "Take the old boy. He sheriffed his life away until they hounded him for his kind heart and now by God he's on the lam, same as if he's spent his time shipping quiff."

"We don't know the setup," I muttered.

"I heard the yack of you two last night. He sounded like he's gone soft in the head, but he was talking right over my ears for awhile there."

Glen turned to me. "I heard too. Both of you set yourselves up as God to judge the Lord's people, but I still think he's a good man, just blind to the Way."

"Look, kid," Max said, "your nose is clean because Mama kept it clean. Give yourself a few years to see if you can keep it that way before you pop wise. You wouldn't believe me, but I was a sanctimonious bastard myself until I got a little dry behind the ears. Hard to believe, ain't it, kid?" Then he looked at both of us, looking through us at himself. "What happened?" he said, "When was it I changed?"

"I'm asking the same question about myself," I answered, and the saying of it forged us a bond he'd long needed.

"Yeah," he said, moving closer. We both hooked our elbows back over the side of the car. "Yeah, it's a funny thing," and here he stopped and couldn't carry it further, nor could I. Finally I realized that staring at the morning sun with the elbows hooked back and chest out wasn't conducive to peering back through the dark alleys of personality. And yet I felt that at the moment we should, for I had a guess on this thing that might help him. So I turned and leaned a bit over the side, looking down at the land as it sped past. Soon both our elbows hooked over, our hands resting on the top, cradling our chins. So we stood, judiciously studying the rush back of brush, and grass, and piles of old ties, and culverts. Finally, from the corner of my eye, I saw him lift his pursed lips from his hands. "Like we was saying," he began in an apologetic tone, "something gets twisted as a guy goes along. Take me now. First I wanted to be a blacksmith and wear a great heavy leather apron and be easy with kids but hard and still awful kind to horses. Yeah, to have my way with iron. Takin' a bar of iron and kinda starin' at it and then takin' it and shovin' it into the forge and rakin' a few scatterings of coke over it, easy and careless—ever seen 'em about there? God, how I wanted to be like that, full of easy wised-up power. Yeah, and takin' the bar out after a slow, lazy pumping of the bellows and layin' it out on the anvil and then—but hell, I got around more later and wanted to be a hotelman with striped pants and a rich air full of knowhow and a little sin. Yeah, sin with rich jewels hid in the creases of broadcloth and satin, and in the creases of corsetted and perfumed women I saw at the entrances of our best hotel. I hadn't forgot the blacksmith, you see. I'll never quit seein' him and mournin' the day I walked into the hotel to take a job as a bellhop. Creases, hell, I know every wrinkle."

"The seamy side?" I asked to make it lighter.

"Naw," he answered, "the seamy side's got a clean bill of health. I'm talkin' about the wisenheimer side, rigged games to take men who feel the need to play—play, Jesus! In my lingo it don't mean the same thing any more. Games—God! Say, do you remember run-sheep-run?"

"Certainly do," I answered. He didn't hear me, I'm sure.

"Knew some swell kids," he went on. "Wonder where they are today? Wouldn't talk like this, 'cept I been thrown out of town like I was rubbish, and knowin' I am don't help. Say, what in hell's got into us anyway?" he wailed in sudden fury. "Ever since I heard you and the old boy start hagglin' about life last night, everybody's been spillin' his guts."

"Maybe it was you that started it," I reminded him. "You were making a mighty clean breast of it as soon as you left Eureka."

"It was like pukin'," he said.

"Maybe we're all sick but Glen."

"We're full of crud," he said, "and gotta get it out."

"Turned inside out a guy isn't so pretty."

"But why turn inside out?" he said. "Why can't a guy keep his crud to himself? Ain't we men enough to button our lips?"

"You look at the men on the streets," I answered. "Look close and you'll see that every man walks along with his broken integrity, thinking it well hidden, while the hell of it tools his face unmistakably. Every man is warped by life except the dedicated ones who work at perpetual motion machines or recipes for contacting God."

"You got any?"

"A few. One is savoring all the most common things."

"What's the other?" he asked, intent, even fierce for it.

"I can't tell you. I'd bat words around trying till the shambles of ideas and clatter of telling would disgust us both, but it's more about tearing down your front and accepting everything from ant trails in the dust to the universe as a boon, as part of the splendor of living, and having no regrets that you're finite."

"Finite?"

"Yes," I said. "Soon dead."

"Do you believe that?"

"I don't know," I answered. "Consciousness is my verity. If there's consciousness past the grave I'll find out in due time."

"Let it pass," Max groaned, wanting to sneer and yet not wanting to. "You've started clawing the air again like you and him was doin' last night. I'm ridin' a train with yahoos." And then he grinned wryly. "Guess you know I ain't complainin'," he said. "Wonder where in hell he is."

By now I was almost certain that if he was on the train he was in that car of lumber I'd put the seal on, or else he'd stayed in Willits. Perhaps he didn't know the cops were after him. He'd just skipped in the manner of all who bum rides on freights when they see railroad bulls. Still, I doubted he'd got in that car in division point, and it without its seal.

I realized I only knew scatterings of him that didn't fit at all. Last night I had figured that when day came I'd take a good look at him, and I hadn't. I was still batting my eyes against the bright morning light when he left. I stared at the fellows in the car without seeing them and then it was my turn to sit on Glen's kit. I sat down and looked back and up at the following boxcar just as he came striding along the catwalk that topped it and stood outlined against the sky.

The wind whipped his great beard about under the pale blue of his hawklike eyes. He was Zeus in rumpled street clothes, he was Moses and Isaiah. With his hat in his hand he stood for some minutes surveying the countryside and the long train's undulant course through it.

I studied to know him with my eyes as I couldn't seem to know him with my mind, but then the outer aspects of a man aren't too complex. I could see, looking up, that he loved life and respected other men and himself. His strongly carved nostrils were flared like an ardent stallion's to take the wind. Once it flung at his beard in a manner that revealed firm lips that age had not turned contentious, just as the years had not slurred him with fat or withered him. Long living was in the crinkling of his skin where each wrinkle showed a habit in one of his ways toward the world. Humor, sadness, thought-fulness, and fury—each in its time had made its little mark upon him; none had gouged him, though if curiosity and acceptance of life could mark a man I believe he'd have been rutted with it. Now it showed only in his eyes.

Along with the wrinkling, the great standing veins on his strange hands gave evidence of the long grip he'd held on things, and time's delicate honings at his temples were hauntingly beautiful.

No, I thought, age is secondary in our old man. Manhood and strong character are his only salients. I glanced at the others, and it was in Max's face and Glen's: we cherished him. He stood some moments more and then, smiling at us, he came down the ladder and once more showed his years as he used my hand to get down into the gondola.

He stood on our tie with us, thumbing shreds of tobacco into his pipe after he had handed me the pouch. I felt proud as I fumbled out my acorn pipe. "Who's got a match?" he asked. "And how's that bender sitting you this morning, Max?"

Max was about to reply when the old man presented him with the bottle. He drained the brief drink left and tossed it over the side.

"R-O-U-G-H!" he grunted. "Hair o' the dog!" and shook himself.

Glen lit the old man's pipe for him, grinning like a chosen courtier. The whole world seemed suddenly to improve; I forgot to look it askance. I handed the pouch back. "Thanks," I said.

He offered what was left to Max and Glen, who said they didn't smoke. In a low voice I told him of my conversation with the cop and where he had gone.

"Pretty much the way I thought," he said, puffing away on his pipe. "There's a reward out for me—a thousand bucks. Trouble is, it don't put me behind bars. I'll be around later to see the guy who picks up that dough, be making it a special point to see him."

"What've they got on you?" I asked.

He smiled, then he took his pipe from where it poked out of his whiskers and laughed outright. "They want me to stop practicing what I preach, not that I preach it."

"Break it down for us," said Max. "What d'ya mean?"

"They want me to quit living as I want to and live as they do. But I don't, and by God I won't." He turned to me. "Why, the talk you and me had last night was straighter and more man-to-man than any I ever had in the better men's clubs my sons belong to, and the trash that spilled at their parties as talk—the women start it even before their coats are off—it's a kind of simpering, and the damned men take it up. Before the evening's over the meeting of people has turned into a facetious, weak-kneed simpering bout."

"You mean you prefer bums to bums?"

"That's it. That's just the size of it. Success seems to make men petulant about the founding things. Yeah, and I've found that there's more fire and eagerness in the eyes of transients and petty thieves an' even killers than there is in the eyes of the successful middle class. I've come to it that when men cease to be savage and impulsive they soon convert even their integrity to suet."

He jabbed his pipestem in amongst his whiskers, had a puff, and took it out and laughed again happily, and his laughter was at the sky, and his beard pointed out like a prophet's should. "Ya understand I ain't naming them all, but I'm naming the majority."

"What is it they're trying to make you do?" I asked.

"Why, come sloping back to my son John's big home in Denver or my younger son's modern house in Omaha. Come home and put on slippers and sit on a fancy chair and rot. The way I see it, a home grew from the need for shelter, a nest for the kids, a wick-i-up against the weather. But as women dominate through the home it becomes a vast extension of the womb, but a womb no longer eager to create, a womb mad to dissolve. In it man's fine fury becomes puttering. Before long he's a mower of lawns, a tinkerer with the impediments of the nest, a wife-adjunct, a trap-licking subspecies."

"Well now," I agreed, "I'll admit that's the way I feel about it when I'm worked up to the point to make a trip, but mine's really not like that. It isn't padded or doilied or dramatized to death. In fact, she's leaned the other way. It's more of a man's house."

"Wonder the other women about haven't found out and tried to strangle her. When you get home you better temper your place and make it a fifty-fifty house. That's the way Mrs. Kindrid's and mine was, and it had real meaning."

"A place to raise sons," I was impelled to say, "an echoing place with the wooden floors bare except in parlor and sewing room."

He looked at me sharply, "You're right again. Sons is all we had, all grown up now and moved away, and the house still stands with echoes enough to choke a man."

"The chaff picks up a little splendor from our imprint."

"I don't get you," the old man said. "Do it with stuff, not words."

"I mean where life has been—empty clam shells, last year's bird's nest, old shoes, abandoned farms, old weed stocks, all engraved with living, and forlorn-seeming without it." But the old man hadn't heard. He was talking to Max.

"Did you know Curly Fenton in Eureka?"

"Yeah, I knew of him."

"So did I," the old man rambled. "Knew him in and out of jail up in Wyoming. He lives by lying old women out of their savings. Got a letter from an old girl he took. I knew her well when I was dirt farming. The damn letter waited for me at my oldest son's place for a year and a half afore I came around. She's dead now. Anyway, I saw him up in Eureka, spotted him down at Ernie's place, and I warned him later—I was on the fool parole board that let him out. You think it was at his place they spotted me?"

"Can't figure Fenton spillin' it," mused Max. "He came into town as a campmeetin' preacher."

"Always did," agreed the old man. "Always waving his arms and shouting for some sect that don't believe in uh—damned if I remember what they don't believe in. It doesn't really matter, just so this special thing puts 'em apart as the anointed ones. Come to think of it, he belonged to several sects. 'Twas handier. Must be riding awful high in that burg to take a chance on his past bein' spilt."

"Say, now I remember," grinned Max. "I ain't exactly up on the doin's of these halo-pitchers."

That reminded me of a hoop-pitching act I'd seen at the old Pantages. I remembered that the girl in the act was slightly knock-kneed in a saving sort of way.

"But now I do remember," Max was saying. "It was in the paper last year. He confessed a bitched-up past."

"Probably told them God had led him to the straight and narrow," the old man muttered. "But the devil tripped him and got him headed on it the wrong way."

"Yeah," said Max, "there was a big hoopla all over town. In the end they forgave him feelin' big and God-like about it and he was in the clear no matter what rumors from his past come sailin' in. What I don't get is the yardbull and that telegram from Omaha."

"My son Larry is chief of police in Omaha. Him and his brother John are bent on me living comfortable in either of their homes. They got this reward out for me—infer I'm doddery, but it won't stick. In some ways this is still a free country, and I ain't about to sit on no fancy cushion. I'm still learnin'—what for I don't know, but I'm still at it. You understand, my boys are right fond of me in their way, only love to them is possession. I see it now as a kind of hands-off thing in essence."

"Mebbe you know there's gonna be plenty back at the tank stop will tell you hopped the train out of there last night."

"The bull'll be along all right," the old man said. "We ain't seen the last of him. Hope the roads is still closed with the storm's trash. I've been dogged like this afore."

He changed the subject with a sudden tilt of his pipe and shoved his Stetson to the back of his head. "You still headin' for Mormon country, Glen?" he asked.

"Well, it's an awful long way to go at this rate," the boy said. "I didn't consider about the Sierras. What do you think of it, Mr. Kindrid?"

The old man put it up to Max. "You worry it around," he said to him.

Max turned, scowling at the kid, rather begrudging him his youth, but the sun coming through the haze shone faintly down on the boy's innocence and caught too at lines of competence showing through the blur of living at home and the fuzz of adolescence.

"I'd try Sacramento," said Max. "I'd hire for little more than board and learn some new angles to this handmade shoe business before I'd set up on my own."

"My father," answered Glen, " was a master shoemaker in Switzerland. I know most all his ways of doing."

"Sure, he's great, but you can always add to your know-how. Sacramento's wild in a way, but it's the capital of the State and it's lousy with tree-jammed streets."

"There's your answer," the old man said. "Take it in easy marches—Sacramento first."

"I'll think about it," Glen answered.

"Yeah," Max grinned. "We'll look the other way and you try it on for size."

Wandering through the hills, the train followed the course of a creek running southward this time.

"Comin' to Ukiah," Max announced. "Don't think the bull had time to get past Willits yet, but he's made the tank by now and he's comin' back hep that you and the old man are on this freight. I don't think he'll catch up at Hopland, but he'll be at Cloverdale waitin'."

But he wasn't. All that met us at Cloverdale was a drenching downpour that soon had us sodden again—all except the old man, whom we'd hid in the boxcar of shifting lumber. In our gondola water from the downpour almost covered the humped up place. Several more bedraggled fellows crawled aboard holding gunnysacks over their shoulders. Steam arose from our soddenness as the train stood on the tracks, but when we were once more under way the wind whipped our body heat away from us. Even the air was saturated, and wouldn't dry our clothing.

A young fellow—somewhat younger than myself—leaned shivering in a striped silk shirt with fancy armbands in a corner of the car and tried to protect his heat by crowding against the cold, steel sides. For a hat he wore the eyeshades of a cardsharp, and his disdain for us was unmerciful: suckers were in a worse plight by being born suckers than he was in his thin pants and silk shirt facing the winter storm. He half crouched himself in that corner of steel and shivered uncontrollably. He had a piece of coal about as big as a baseball, and he kept one foot out of the water by putting it on that lump of coal. He shifted it from foot to foot and finally tried to balance on it with both feet out of the water, but that shoved him up three inches higher into the winds that whisked over the sides of the car. So he quit that and knuckled himself all over in a vain attempt to speed up his circulation, all the while staring in a fury at us unpredatory ones around him.

From the talk in the car I got it that he came up from Fort Bragg in the caboose. The short line crew knew him well enough to do that for him. But now, unknown among strangers, only he knew that he was one of the elite, and that didn't help. He'd probably been in charge of the backroom tables up at Joe's or down at Louis' before trouble drove him out of town.

We moved slowly past another Eureka-bound freight on the siding. It was piled with sodden bums like ourselves. They wanted to know why we headed toward Frisco. "You guys crazy or just ignorant?" they yelled.

"You'll keep warm around the big bonfires up there," someone replied, "but what you gonna eat?"

"Ain't there clams, crabs, and lots of salmon up there?" a wistful little fellow wanted to know.

"Maybe," a character whined out on our car, "but how you gonna get 'em?"

"Why, they're easy got, the way I hear," the fellow cried back as our cars drew apart.

"Nothin's easy got, ya fool," a big bum on our train yelled, "and natives is all they take care of up there."

"Wait'll ya get to Frisco," wafted back to us over the grind of progress. "You'll be lucky to be floppin' in the clink."

"Warm clink," that same reminiscent voice said behind me somewhere. He'd stuck the train through, that sad bleater of last night. I couldn't spot him. I hadn't the slightest idea what he looked like.

"They're lousy fleabags, though," I remarked, hoping he'd respond. But he didn't. I never found who it was that conceived of jails as homey.

After we gained way again some of the bums scattered to find better riding places, but they soon filtered back, walking bent-kneed on the jerking catwalks atop the cars. There were no better riding spots, for the train was all sealed boxcars now with the exception of our gondola. "Better to have wet feet than have the wind blow your head off," one of them summed it up.

Way past half way home, I told myself, and stood the tie stoutly. Then I got to worrying about the old man locked up in that lumbercar. It was safe in there, sure, if a guy didn't get down in a hole. But the way we'd strewn boards getting the trapped fellows out had made a pitted, teetering shambles of it. Finally it bothered me to a point I felt I had to go see if he was safe.

Glen and Max held my place on the tie by standing my pack on it, while I scuttled over the car tops and unlocked the little door in the end of the old man's hideaway. He squirmed out at once over the clattering space between the cars and we fixed the tape back so it looked like it had never been tampered with and then made our way back to our tie in the gondola.

"How was it?" I asked him when we got back.

"Some of it slithered down as we jerked to a stand at Cloverdale," the old man said. "We had that stuff piled in there like jackstraws. I'm tellin' ya, I want no more of that car. They ain't enough pot-bellied railroad dicks west of the Rockies to make me dodge in there again."

I was glad we'd fixed the seal, for the rest of the bums couldn't know which car it was, the train had been shifted and changed so much since we hopped it in Eureka.

"You send a card to your missus afore you left?" the old man asked, fondling his nose.

"Yep," I answered, "she knows I'm coming. Look," I went on, "why don't you come along too and stop with us for the winter? Our place is only four miles from where this trip ends. We got food aplenty for the winter and an extra room and, being three miles from the nearest neighbor, a need for company."

He twisted around and glared at me: "Hell, Willie, if it's a home I wanted I'd of given myself up to the Willits dick and rode east in style."

"But this ain't the same," I answered. "Nothing against your son's friends, but the folks we name as friends ain't simperers or Rotarians or Masons. And we live plain. We did it from choice before the damned Depression made it compulsory."

He was reared back now, his fierce eyes glaring at me. He seemed like a great eagle, as if he were about to strike and deal me a fatal blow with his nose. "Drop it," he gritted, and turned from me on the tie.

But I couldn't seem to stop myself. The words choked their way up my throat and into my mouth and I let them stumble out. "How much longer you think you can keep travelling without a layup?" I asked him.

He turned and scanned me up and down coldly and then made a point of talking to Max as if I wasn't standing between them.

"Know your way around L.A.?" he asked him.

"I know L.A. better than I know women," Max replied.

The old man pondered that, looking coldly over my head, but didn't answer. Finally he seemed to forget us all, not that anything else appeared to steal his attention. He just sagged into one of those voids, one of those mental hammocks the old people use when confronted with the questions they couldn't find an answer for in a lifetime of living.

The train rocked on. The vibrations of our gondola's passage kept the surface of the water our tie stood in alive with infinitesimal ripples. We sped past this hummock and that ditch, we rolled past the little kingdoms of farmers, we pushed along through Mendocino County and the high clouds looking down saw our train as a slow centipede inching down over the long land of California.

I studied the old man's hands. I came back from my remoteness, but he didn't come back from his, though his body was there and his hands. One rested on the top of the gondola side. It was a big hand with massive palm and scarred, angular knuckles. The funny thing about it was that the strong fingers tapered excessively to delicate nails set in fingertips smallish almost to deformity. It aroused my curiosity, but his silence was so infectious that we all went inside ourselves for awhile, away from the chill world, into our memories.

Glen's lip trembled over some bit of homesickness. Max stared into some debacle of his past grimly and finally faced himself, I think, for he said "So what," and it seemed to still— for the time at least—the floundering inside. The old man stayed pasted into the little death that had caught up with him.

Looking out at the winter scene made my heart ache for spring, and I was soon lost in memories of its leafing out and of the welling up of new life from the seeds and skeletons of the old.

WE TRAVELED ACROSS A plain where remote farmhouses appeared to be abandoned of all but the plumes of smoke from their chimneys, but the winter land repelled thinking on it. Again I fell to wondering at the way my body went on and on without food and the way it seemed to need so little sleep. I'd slept enough in the mountains, God knows, with the woods darkening at five.

I'd have wood for the night's fire in, and I'd urinate before turning at last indoors. I'd stand there in that bit of a clearing around the old stump of a tree the builder had constructed the cabin from, and the faint smell of urine would come up from the ground as I stared high to the west over the canyon wall where the irregularities of the timbered crest stood into the last, rusty light of sunset. Hunger would be in me to be with Tom and Jim in the cabin two miles down across the river, or I'd lengthen my scope and yearn toward the store at Emby where four or five Emby men might be sitting around the stove drinking the brew they made together as a community affair. Past that was the wonder of home and family, but too far, too removed: that was the miracle only to be taken out and cherished in the time before sleep. God! The hunger for companionship that would well in me as night closed in that canyon!

Then I'd give up, I'd admit to myself that I was locked in this place by the night, for travel even with the lantern was extremely dangerous because of the cliffs for the first two miles below me. I'd peer down the dark corridors of the forest then, sniffing the cold drafts that came down from the snow above, sniffing for cat smells or bear, some bear still ranged, though most had denned for the winter. Why? I'd ask myself abjectly—why? You belong to a gregarious species. Why can't you be like the others? And in agony I'd answer that I didn't know. Maybe it started from a book read in childhood, a catch phrase, a poem maybe. Or maybe the seeing of spring through young eyes endorsed all outdoors environment as friendly. How can I tell what caused the first deviation? I only know it moves me to splendors, and sometimes to agonies of loneliness like this.

I'd turn from the yearnings and the arguments and that wafting chill from the snow and, carrying yet another armful of dry fuel from the chopping block, I'd enter the cabin to throw it down before the hearth, closing the door and starting the fire. And when its light was dancing on the cabin walls I'd cook my meal and the smell of coffee, and of beans and bacon and my pipe, would fill the void of loneliness and the moment would be all right. Some tune would come to my mind and, humming it, I'd set out the steaming food, and warmth and coziness would be in the forlorn shack. And after eating, the tune still in my mind, I'd try the words, though softly, and take from its hiding place the stone I was sure was a ruby, and my tiny poke of gold flakes and dust, and the nugget as big as a pea, and dream and plan—me, a mite, isolated in a canyon from my kind while the stars wheeled in their order through our particular eternity—and owls would hoot to one another from across the clearing.

A fellow had been looking up into my eyes as he stood down on the gondola's slosh of water. I'd been aware of his

staring but loath to leave my memories of the canyon. I saw
him, yet I started to sag into the usual inertia or reserve. Then
I remembered my hunger for companionship in the canyon.
Don't turn from it now, I muttered inwardly; he wants to talk.
I looked into his eyes, leaving that view of the canyon that
now, having passed through it, I must carry with me always. I
looked into his bright, shallow stare as it caught at me coming
outside of myself like a fellow in his bathrobe searching the
stoop for the morning paper. And seeing, I blinked at the *now*
of the moment. He surveyed the scene for me.

"Making to come into Asti," he said.

"Yep," I replied, "it looks like it."

He moved a step closer. "You got a big pack there," he
announced in a tone at once fiercely loyal and yet somehow
diffident to the other three standing the tie.

"Too big and clumsy," I answered.

With slightly curved lip he surveyed his fellows standing in
the water. "There's plenty in this 'dola," he said, "what
couldn't hump it a mile."

"Kinda fagged myself," I answered. "We all are."

"I ain't," he said, "I ain't at all."

But he knew he was—not as much as some of us, but still
weary. "You're coming in from Fort Bragg, aren't ya?" I asked,
not caring, but wanting to pass the time.

"Yeah," he said. "Heard there was work up there in the
woods. Weren't none though." He spat down into the water.
"Jest some more of them crappy rumors ya hear around Howard
Street."

"You a faller?" I asked, naming the aristocrat of woodsmen.

He squared off from me. "Do I look like a hillbilly, friend?
You see any moss growing out of my ears? You're talking same
as they did in Fort Bragg. Hell, I'm better'n any faller or
bucker I ever seen in Frisco."

"It's a pretty exacting trade," I said, "and you got to have
the knack."

That was his sore spot but, knowing what he was, I didn't give a damn.

"Exacting trade," he exploded. "Damned if you don't believe that crap. You're one of those weak bastards that learn a trade just like the bosses want. Me, I play the angles and get by without that bilge."

The old man spoke up. "Willie," he said, "what you are sticks out all over you. You're the crumb that they hire outside and bring onto the job some sad morning of spar tree loggin' and you say you know how but don't, figgerin' to do like the others do, aping 'em till you figger you can get by on your own, and you're in there where every man jack's life depends on the other fellow's savvy. The gang smells a rat but the whistle's blowin' and they gotta bring their quota up to the spar tree or else and jobs are scarce.

"You wise-guy around and go at it scared and looking out just for Willie, and the noon whistle ain't blowed afore some man's lost his leg or his life or the gear is all torn up and the superintendent saves you from being kicked to death and they send a flunky to drive you back to the railroad, and on your way out you sneer at exacting trades. Now get the hell away from this tie and downwind where I can't smell you! I can get along with pret' near every kind of human but jokers of his stripe," he said to Max. And then to the smart guy, who was working up to what he figured was a safe rage at an old man, "And you try to lay a mitt on me, figuring I'm old, and I'll develop a little hole between your eyes so quick it won't bother you at all."

The wise guy moved away snarling and the old man was silent. Those bums who'd heard were noncommittal. Nobody cared much if the old man had a gun on him and certainly no one wanted to find out.

The drizzle that was coming down fogged around us. I knew how we looked as we banged along: a rusty gondola, the men standing hunched in sodden grey except for the fellow in the candy-striped shirt, and we on the tie a head higher than the

110

rest with the old man, black hat and all, prodding up as the only thing notable in the car. Again we left a shower, but the wind was so dank that the only thing we missed was the impact of raindrops.

"Merciful God," said a man near us, "let's get off next time she stops and hole up."

"Hole up where?" another fellow asked. "Ever stop along here? They give you the bum's rush back onta the train. You couldn't pile off if you wanted to."

"How about Santa Rosa?" someone asked.

"Sure, they let you off there, but so's you can take the short line toward the valley. Anyway, they hound you outta town."

"How you so wised up on this?" another shivering individual asked, wringing out the stocking cap he was wearing.

"I gotta aunt lives in the next county and I pick up odd jobs 'round here. Ya might say her place is my headquarters—that is, if she'd let me in."

The young fellow with the silk shirt had finally crumbled his piece of coal from changing it constantly from one foot to the other. He was beside himself with fury at his predicament but, with jaws clamped against the shivering that shook him, he couldn't afford to cuss.

At Geyserville we stood woebegonely in our car, except for the fellow whose headquarters was in the next county. He slipped off and hooked a scoop shovel that was leaning against the freight house and, as soon as we were out of town, started scooping up and shoveling water out of the car. We took turns at it—all but the gambler had a brief fling at it—and we all warmed a bit from the exertion while he watched the process with the patent disdain of a nonproducer. We got the water down so there were just puddles on the battered steel floor. The air began to chill, the sky arched its grey cap much higher, the sun-starved groves and farms showed no flare of color or shadow, and the landscape—the trees and barns—seemed dead, or carved of stone. I grew sick at heart watching the land—I, who valued it above commerce with my fellows, turned from it to the car's freight of misery, and was renewed.

Max was going over his exodus with one of the bums from Eureka. Glen had left the tie and, at the side of the car, stared eastward as if trying to fathom the unseen Sierras. I glanced furtively at the old man: his eyes were closed and his solid body rocked a bit on his legs to the jarring of the train. I thought of William Cullen Bryant and Joaquin Miller. I peered into the mask he presented, tarrying over the lines of high breeding but never unaware of some savage gut-founded strain that moulded power into the essence of him. I noted several scars—maybe of combat, I thought, or perhaps horse-thrown and dragged. I was muddling over these possibilities when, like a chicken, he opened one eye and regarded me. No expression touched his face; there was just his one eye open, looking at me and, after a moment, closing the way a chicken's does.

Come on out, I wanted to yell. Tell us what you've learned and reaffirm what you brought to it. My hunger must have been loud, for the eyelid fluttered, though after that his face became more remote than ever. Glen still stared at the low eastern mountains beyond which, one hundred miles away, were the snow-clogged Sierras. I became convinced that he would go on past Sacramento and shoe the sauntering Mormons, though I was never to know.

I stepped down from the tie and stood among the others and at once felt as they had looked when I watched them from my perch, my promontory of a tie, eight inches off the deck. We jarred over the switch of a siding where cars of oak cordwood stood waiting a better price. The cardsharp's green eyeshade blew off, sailed the length of the car, slapped against the end of the following boxcar, and was gone. It seemed the loss heightened his tension. He crammed himself into a cold steel corner, squatting there above a rusty puddle while the steel contacts sucked more of the precious heat from his blood. I could fancy from experiences of my own how it went: extremities numbed, stomach and gut getting cooler and cooler, heart and lungs feeling the chill, and spinal cord, the marrow of backbone, becoming stiff tallow from the draining away of heat faster than the body could produce it.

I disliked his kind and yet...quit quibbling, another part of me said. Do unto others as you'd be done by. It's a motto, I sneered, a framed, hand-embroidered motto. And anyway, he makes his living belying that sentiment. But I went over to him and took off and handed him my coat. He struck it to the floor in an agony of hatred. I picked it up and handed it to him again. He stood up from it and the wind hitting his back from over the side of the car cut at the freezing flesh so that he dropped down again into his crouch. I put the coat around his shoulders.

"You'll die in this wind without some protection."

He tried to curse me but couldn't open his mouth against his cramped jaw muscles. Again he stood up as if to slug at me, but remained still and let me button the coat around him. It was a heavy coat and long, reaching half way to his knees, and it was lined. Wet, sure, but lined with blanket. I buttoned the last button and turned, feeling the bite of the wind through the wool of my shirt and underwear. I was also aware of the others, and though I looked no one in the eye I felt guilty before the several projections that I made of their probable attitudes:

"Mr. Lucky, with the biggest pack and coats to hand out..."

"A soft bastard with ideals like posies, no less. Him a standin' there with us bums and puttin' on airs like them we scrounge handouts from..."

I'd done it again. The belonging I'd felt in the car, torn and strewn with one simple, decent urge. Yeah, I prodded myself, that other wistful me, you did it again just a bit ago with the old man. Face it, the inner torment went on, can you be one of them? You want to be, sure, but can you? Is there any place where you can really belong? Is there, say, a publication for your particular kind—Mink Breeder's Digest, Gun Moll's

Monthly, Pervert's Periodical, New Masses, Fortune—where you can really fit?

I dropped it with towering annoyance and thought only of life in this gondola. I didn't look at them nor did I move down the car and take my place upon the tie, but turned instead to the side and looked with Glen at the range of hills east of us.

The highway ran parallel to the tracks across a little plain and on the highway, racing us in an ancient Model T roadster, was a young farmer and his wife with two flaxen-haired little girls, along with a crated turkey in a homemade rumbleseat. The top of the roadster was made from a sheet of corrugated tin roofing, and the little girls were each eating a great white-fleshed rosy apple. The turkey, with head and neck forced out between slats, viewed the scene with faded dowager alarm. Pacing beside our particular car, they all looked up at us. They smiled, and the wife and little girls waved, but the farmer held to the wheel like mad, for he had to drive his rattletrap of a Ford too fast in order to keep up with the train. Exhilaration pricked him up while fear cramped his hands on the wheel, and he turned his head carefully from time to time, slued his eyes around and looked at us. One of the little girls tried to throw an apple into our car. The first one fell short, so she threw the one she'd been eating and it fell among us. She had hardly done this when the road swerved away from the tracks, and in no time they were a black little rig far out on the plain, and then we burst into a defile between hills that opened on another flat below.

The big man who had picked up the apple was wiping it upon his sleeve, brushing away bits of coal that were stuck in the bruised place where it landed. Then he turned the apple to see where the little girl had been eating. Her teeth marks were in the snow of its meat.

"Had plenty of wing on her to sling it clean in here," he said.

The red apple with the snow of its meat brought to each man, I felt, a vision of the rosy-cheeked, laughing girl and her sister. I considered the car full of men and thought to myself: But we're bedraggled by times, by circumstances. Do you want men to be as artless as little girls? Hell no, I answered myself, but I do wish that we seemed less like dead men.

"How old do you figger she was?" a grey, sodden-coated fellow was asking his neighbor.

"Kee-rist," the other fellow sniggered, "I sure would like to 'a' found out—eleven maybe, or twelve, coulda been thirteen."

"Aw c'mon—that's too young," the first man said. At which the other fellow gave him such a look of derisive savagery that he turned to the rail feeling at the moment ashamed of his qualified decency.

The big man with the apple still stared at it, holding it up a bit as if it were extraordinary. Finally he addressed himself rather self-consciously to the car in general.

"Well, boys, I figger she threw it so's him that got it could eat it. Well," he went on haltingly, "here goes," and he bit a great bit into the red cheek of the apple. Then he withdrew his teeth from it and, forgetting us, got out his pocketknife and reverently cut away the place that the little girl had been eating and put it in his pocket. After that he ate the apple, core and all, in the manner of stock.

Just before we entered a gap between more hills, I saw the corrugated iron on the old Ford far behind us, a flick of light on its incongruous roof that touched the retinas of my tired eyes and freighted me with warm connotations. I felt the family was warm the way a slut dog and her cuddled mass of puppies is warm, that the father was stout for his family against the importunities of fate, and that mother and girls of awkward culture and dress were sturdy and graceful, and that all their laughter was kind.

Our wheels groaned on the spiked-down curves of the rails and a shoulder of the hills obscured them from me forever. Did they, the mother and girls, bloom their lives in some sheltered cove of the hills while he curried slanting, rock-fenced fields? Were there geese and banty hens and turkey gobblers in the door? Were the few soft thunders of the horses moving in their stalls at night a comfort to the family as they lay in their beds awaiting sleep?

I wanted to go to the old man and somehow, through guesswork, build with him their life and home. The old man could build the structure, the land and how they got it, the forty acres rented from a cross-eyed psalm-singing farmer on the other side of the ridge. Where he got his wife and how they built the house. I'd fill in with a secondhand organ they kept in the kitchen because the roof needed reshingling over the parlor. And the way they got such a fine dog to herd the cows: "Just by pickin' up a stray." And how last year in late spring a little boy came from over the hill and worried around up in the oaks above the barn until the little girls went up and played with him. How their laughter helped the leaves deck the grove with the exuberance of early summer.

I looked around for the old man. He was right beside me and almost looking at me—or, rather, our glances crossed somewhere between us and were not allowed to meet head-on. Then he turned his gaze slightly and was looking past me into the side of the hill we were rounding. His stilted awareness showed only in some variance of his beard where it clothed his mouth, as if forbidding lines of no compromise setting in his face the beard and mustache were tugged to conform but could not.

No, I thought, he hates my guts.

God, how cold the wind was, how slow the trek!

Again in my mind I was walking the last mile on the winding road home. It was dark and my feet rattled the stones of the road. It was a road of ceaseless turnings, and in the dark I couldn't make out which turn I was on. I tried to ease the dark by conjuring up Nordi's face, but it wouldn't come. I could make a luminousness in the dark, a vague glow of a face, but that was all.

I looked around. The gambler was beating life into himself as he swung his arms and jogged his legs. My coat was buttoned tight around him, collar up hiding his ears. He was coming out of it. He would make the grade unless pneumonia caught up with him.

The fellow who said he worked the angles was talking to several others. They glanced my way so much that I felt that I was their topic. So what? Sure, I made a fool move with the coat, but the first guy who got fancy with me was going to be in trouble.

What is there about the jerk and sway of travel, the strange and ever-changing scene, that throttles the ego but still pulls the transient somehow into a more whole being? Is it that the rub of new vistas burnishes certain elements of man that in static living are dulled with somnolence?

The pull of home was strong at me, while that solitary life I'd led in the mountains filled my heart with such poignancy for the beloved wilderness I was leaving. I can't say that I had consciously personalized various environments, and yet I felt friendly and related. Not just to family and to the world of men. I felt as a rather close cousin to the meanest of opossums and to the inflexible-minded flexible snake; and the trees and cliffs, the crags and knolls and rivers, were to me but second cousins from my Mother Nature's side of the family.

The angle worker was moving over to me, swaggering a bit. "Lady Bountiful," he grated out loudly, "you must have gifts for all us bums in your pack."

"Jesus!" I said. "You again."

"You're damn right—me! And you're gonna like it 'fore I'm through. Ya know," he went on, "I'll bet you were the boss's white-haired boy till the whole job folded, and I'd bet my shirt you got a spoon-shaped tongue."

I caught him flush on the jaw and knocked him sprawling, but he jumped up again and swaggered back to me.

"Just what I thought," he snarled. "That was more of a push. It ain't got no snap, cuz you're pooped." He was right. As soon as I hit him I knew the trek had worn me to a frazzle. "You know," he went on, "I bet you got a lot of things in that pack that me and my friends can use. Pooped and a softy to boot. I'm gonna like this. First you're gonna hand me what I want outta that pack of yours and then next time she slows I'm gonna kick your ass off this train. The old guy ain't gonna help ya. I see how ya gall him. Bring your pack here and open it up."

I moved abjectly as if to get it and kicked him in the shins before he could react. Then I grabbed him and stamped on his feet and held on and kneed him in thc groin before he dragged me down. Trouble was, each punishing move I made was slow and weak and did little damage. He reached out his mouth to bite my ear, but I butted his nose. While he groped for my eyes we rolled over and over in the puddle. He was burly, though a bit lighter than me, and he was tired too, while I was a shambles from my fourth day of merciless homing. We rolled, straining weakly at each other. It seemed I could barely flounder my body around and avoid his fingers at my eyes. Then he was under me. I swung at his jaw and hit the deck instead, driving flakes of coal into my knuckles. Somehow he got on top of me and almost got me, stabbing his fingers into the cheek just below my eyes. I wrapped my arms around his neck and protected my face with his. His cheek was under my mouth. I took a great bite and held on, grinding. He screamed, floundering on me like a chicken with its head cut off. By God, I could still bite. My leaden arms couldn't fend his blows, but I could still bite like a dog.

I was on top now and stayed there trying to sever his cheek from his face. His companions were kicking me in the back and legs when I got my hands in his hair, let go of my bite, and beat his head savagely against the deck. They pulled me off of him and one lit astride me while the other continued kicking. I got the man astride me by the windpipe but I couldn't throttle him, and I got kicked in the neck. The guy on top of me was aiming a heavy blow at my head when through the red of fury I saw a great hand with tapered fingers reach down over his

118

face, hook two fingers in his nostrils, and jerk him backward off of me.

I rolled over painfully and on hands and knees swayed erect. Through the red I couldn't see at once who it was who'd kicked me. Over in the corner my last assailant lay on his back stunned and bleeding from badly torn nostrils. The old man was walking across the deck, carrying the angles bum by his face, a finger at the edge of both eyesockets and his thumb under his chin, while the bum tried feebly to grab at his wrists. He pitched him on top of the stunned man, then he cornered the fellow who'd been kicking me, grabbed him by the neck, and flung him onto the other two.

"The first time she slows," he said to the angles man, "you get you and your pards down that boarding ladder or I'll pitch you out on your head."

He came over to me smiling. "Yep," he said, "you'll do. I had you kind of halfway sized up, but weren't sure. I'll get the tent out of your pack and we can wrap you in that. Anything broken?"

I couldn't answer for awhile, but when he was getting the tent around me I was able to mutter, "Thanks."

"You want your coat?"

I shook my head. "I lent it to him," I finally said.

We ran through a little belt of warm air, though where it came from was past understanding. We stood on our tie and, though soaking wet and beat up, I looked down at the ordered white folds of the tent I was wrapped in and felt slightly Roman.

"He figgered you was a softy," the old man announced, laughing congenially. "You should see his cheek—and him try-ing to put the bite on you." He laughed again as if at an enor-mous joke, and his hand was on my shoulder shaking me gently. "If it's still open," he said, "I'll take you up on your offer. Like to warn your kid to keep away from your teeth."

AT A SIDING WHERE we picked up several cars of cordwood the angles man and his two companions left us. Soon after when we were underway again, a northeast wind came driving between the hills and in a short time we were in a heavy, steady gale. The rest of the fellows in the car crowded around our tie, sitting on it between our feet and thus keeping down out of the weather.

I was then that I noticed the freezing gambler was gone— with my coat. No one had seen him leave; he must have slipped over the opposite side of the car as we all watched the angles man and his buddies make their exit. My good coat was gone, but then what did I expect?

We came through straggling lights into Santa Rosa at early dusk. We arrived with the old man and my pack hid in the box-car of teetering lumber. It took a lot of talking to get him back into it. I let on to the rest of the bunch that me and the old man were going up the short line to Sacramento, and I got off before the train stopped and from a safe distance watched the yard bulls eyeing the bums as they came over the side and stretched their legs.

The fat bull from Willits was there. He sauntered around examining the train and every bum. He was still working alone, so evidently hadn't divulged his secret, and even at a distance I could see how keyed up he was. I saw him corner a bum heading into town, questioning and threatening. Finally he headed off toward the short line freight with sort of a trot to him. It was pulling out the same time that we did.

For three quarters of an hour in a howling wind and deep dusk we bums trailed about town with the cops and the railroad bulls on our heels. We trudged up and down arc-lit streets, staring as if hypnotized into the lighted windows where families ate together in security, and the dicks and bulls yawned as they sauntered behind.

I was shaking, as the gambler had been, in my dripping clothes. Finally down near the tracks I found a good place to jump the freight as it rumbled out of the railroad yards. I waited there and the feeling grew in me that unless I fortified myself with something I would never make it home. Steal something? But what? How? Beg something—some bread? I, beg? I'd starved before but never begged. Die then, stagger into a heap and die. No! Smash a window and get thrown into jail and be fed in the dry cell, resting on warm blankets? But that wouldn't get me to Bunky and Nordi. Beg a glass of hot water, drink down some heat—B.T.U.'s. B.T.U.'s—God, how removed! Would they jail me for begging a glass of water? Beg some heat—"Please, sir, a little heat to warm my gut." I would; I had to. When the first whistle blew, before she pulled out, then I'd beg.

I picked the house that I'd tackle. I could see the family at supper. Down the street a cop waited. And then the train blew its shrill warning whistle. Beg? Whine, crawl? Just water—you don't have to crawl for water. Up the walk I go; I'm on the porch; I've rung the bell and the cop has seen and is yelling at me as he comes. A man opens the door and heat and light flow forth. He switches on the porch light.

"Good evening," he says.

Down the street the cop yells again.

"Look," I say, "I'm going through on a freight. Give me a big glass of hot water so I can keep going." He gets the picture. A guy's in a tough spot. "Wait," he says and disappears. But the bull's on the porch with his hand on my arm when the guy comes back. He hands me a big glass of piping hot water.

"Drink it," he says, and I do, while he talks the cop out of the pinch. The water's hot as hell with a shot of whiskey in it. It burns in my throat and just plain blooms in my stomach. It's a glass full of hope.

"Thanks," I say, "I'll make it now."

Then the train starts to move and I look at him again. "You haven't any idea," I say.

"I can guess," he replies. "Hurry and catch her."

And I stumble down his steps and out on the ballast, and as the gondola comes slowly up I hit the ladder sure and my hands on the rung haven't got the palsy. I've got some confidence and don't feel a bit like a beggar.

When Santa Rosa's lights were dim behind us I got the old man out of the boxcar once more. This time we were almost caught by a brakeman. He flashed his light on us between cars and on the aluminum tape of the little door's hasp. Everything looked okay and he ordered us up the gondola.

"It's safe up there," he said. "This old guy shouldn't be riding between cars."

In the gondola the bums had moved our tie up by the humped-up place in the deck. They'd covered up the humped-up place, which was dry now, with layers of old newspapers that somebody had garnered. It kind of killed the cold of the steel deck. They were all sitting there out of the wind jammed together for warmth on the hump and the tie.

Glen and Max had a place saved for us and we jammed in with the rest like herd animals. We banged on through the cold night, shoving closer and closer to each other to confound the cold, fingering drafts. Little was said. Once more I got out my tent and wrapped it about those that took the east wind as it whipped down over the sides of our car.

Finally Max said, "You see the bull?"

"Sure," I answered, and I told him about it.

The old man was silent; we all were, if you can conceive of quiet in the steady racket of the freight's passage. We huddled closer in the dark, a good dozen of us pressed into a yeasty cake of men from which all ferment had been driven by the cold. Somewhere in our mass a boy whimpered. It wasn't Glen, who pressed close against my shins while another fellow kept jamming closer against my legs, the bulging pocket of my trouser sewn around the stone I thought might be a ruby and a few pinches of gold dust that I must bring back to Nordi inviolate. The old man was back to back with me while Max was jammed against my right side. Once in awhile someone started to speak of an experience or a desire, like a dry bed or food or whiskey. Once in awhile a fellow would roll and puff a cigarette made of reprocessed snipes. The smoke smelled warm, so warm I felt better. Glen was shivering again. I wondered why the smoke was unable to help him. The old man would cough once in awhile and I could hear the resonance in his chest through his back and mine.

He turned to ask how far my place was from the railroad, and I told him again that it was not quite four miles.

Again it began to rain, at first scarcely more than a mist that for the moment seemed to make the harsh wind less bitter, then it turned into drops, drops that had a whang to them in the wind. It changed into a steady, heavy rain that the wind caught and flung into every protected nook of our man mass. It blew in our ears, up under the brims of our soggy hats; it flung down our necks and soon, drenching us, it invaded our armpits and navels. Though I'd lived through four days in conditions as clammy as the love of two flounders, this night's drenchings made me forget all past soakings.

Then a guy got a cramp in the big muscle of his leg, jerked upright and hobbled groaning over the others as he gained an uncluttered place in which to limp and grumble it away. Without thinking, we imperceptibly closed ranks on the space he'd left.

From then on it never ceased raining until just before we'd reached Tiburon. After a gnawing, miserable space of time, the old man pushed away those that encumbered him, got to his feet and, tapping my shoulder, waited for me behind the dark, steaming sprawl of our companions.

"Let's shovel water," he said. "It's rising in the car."

We worked turns about with the shovel. I could barely manage it, but the old man seemed unaffected by the lack of food or shelter. The beating I'd taken had lamed my arms, and my neck was stiff where I'd been kicked. It was a rough go, that shoveling, but it did increase circulation. Turn and weak turn about, we shoveled until again there were only puddles.

"Now," the old man said, "we gotta keep moving."

We walked from end to end of the car, and when I faltered he steadied me until the dizziness that caught at me passed and I could trudge on my own.

"How long you been on this push toward home?" he asked.

I replied that I'd been traveling three days and part of the nights before I got to the railroad.

"When was your last meal?"

I couldn't remember; then it came. "It was the breakfast second morning out from my cabin. Something got my food bag while I slept—a bear or a family of skunks—but I had a big bannock in the frying pan and they didn't take that. Had seven cents to buy some day old bread in Santa Rosa, figured that would pull me through. But I left the pennies in my coat. It serves me right."

"No wonder you're pooped," he said. "Wish I had some figs left, but I ain't."

"Oh, I'll make it," I replied. "I feel better now."

"Yeah," he answered. "Well, you've used up any hidden pockets of energy in that scrap. Lucky for you you're near home."

We walked very slowly in the swaying car, stopping often, moving just enough to keep a vestige of warmth in our bodies.

"Look at 'em," the old man said, surveying the huddle of our companions. "That gambler who swiped your coat 'uz all in a piece in his predatory way, and these in their crowding is a lot like a mass of puppies."

"They seem no stranger to me," I responded, "than those made effete by a life of luxury."

"I suppose you're right," he said. "You know, Clyde, the whole spectrum of mankind seems clear and simple to me right now. Guess this trip is wearing me down to the point where I'll take on silly, easy answers."

The jar of the brakes slammed through the train and slowly we came to a stop and then, after they had flipped a switch, turned into a siding and waited. Those on the deck squirmed restlessly and some groped up and stood at the rail, staring off into the blustery night. It didn't prick me up when the train we waited for sounded its approach, but when it passed us slowly it blocked away the wind and a waft of heat from its engine was a second balm. We saw the bright, lovely, open firedoor. In the baggage car a wispy, mustached man sorted stuff in his shirtsleeves.

All the bums were at the rail now, staring hungrily into the protected comfort of the baggage car, and then we sodden ones were looking into the passing diner, empty but for three Negro waiters who sat at the corner table laughing with good-natured, easy languor at a fourth who was clearing the tables. Oh, how marvelous the lights and the white order of that car! Its quiet wheels, like those following, rolled the tracks heavily, sedately bearing designed and conditioned comfort. In the next car people rested on the velvet—flashy traveling salesmen, a milltown owner and his son going home, women with children, and a few haunted faces of people whom fate had rooted out from the familiar and was casting into a new and callous environment.

126

In another car, along with four at poker and an elderly farmer with his wife asleep, were a couple much in love: young with shining faces and the ardent awkwardness of honeymooners. Another car and another and another, faster now, rolled by, each bearing its freight of harried or happy people under bright lights that for us out in the dark and cold seemed to magnify and explain each face as they passed us.

It awakened me. They were us—our fellow humans riding these same tracks under different conditions. Fate, ability, accident put them there and us beggared ones out in the storm, but we were the same. Men like me and those around me made those cars and laid the tracks. Some of us would in the near future ride on plush, and many of those pillowed now from the rude world would hunt the sanctuary of a freight car before the lapse of too much time.

The wind struck hard after the train passed and we all went back to the sodden newspapers on the deck and shoved even tighter together. But we said very little, each man still seeing, I suspect, the comfort and luxury of those coaches. Time went on. Again the old man and I got up to walk.

"Four miles!" he said as I limped back and forth before him. "I don't think you can walk four miles without a slug of grub and some sleep."

"Don't worry," I answered after a moment. "I could make it, but I'm going to get a friend of mine to drive us out. You'll like it out there," I pushed on after a pause. "I'm going to get a bang out of introducing you to Carl and Bob and Crescentia Majoris. I'll butcher a pig. There's one that should be ready."

"How are you fixed for spuds?" the old man asked.

"Five sacks," I answered. "Raised 'em myself, and I got a keg of kraut and homebrew—enough for all winter."

"Hell's fire!" the old man exclaimed. "You maybe got enough for us to forget this trip on. How about your wife though?"

"She's always eager for someone to stay with us. It's lonely for her out there. The nearest woman neighbor is three miles and no friend of hers anyway."

127

"I could use a big feed or two," the old man remarked. "Had me a big steak dinner—two T-bones and double everything—before I left Eureka. I'd won several hands of stud down at Ernie's. Ate this big meal and went back and lost even the money I had stashed away to get out of town on." He made some gesture in the darkness. "Who cares?" he said. "I was watching their faces while they played—them in the game and the kibitzers and idlers. I was trying to figger by looking at them if we were worthwhile—the race, I mean. Felt I almost had the answers—kind of an enigma with a little shine on it, like the answers have when you first come on them. Before you start poking holes through 'em and looking for a new, glowing absolute."

"You lost from being a philosopher," I reproved him.

I was swept with a sense of futile annoyance. Why in hell, I asked myself, did I have to hold out that seven cents so long. If I'd have used it in Hopland or Cloverdale I'd have half a loaf under my belt now. And what an absurd fool I'd been with the coat.

Petaluma seemed deserted. It was about nine-thirty, but the cops must have been on the other side of town rolling up the sidewalks for the night. I took my pack and moseyed over to a feed store near the tracks. I could see no one about and wandered quietly under a cavernous, covered, loading space. It was drying there with the smell of hay. At the back I found a door. It was ajar. I trembled as I eased my pack off and crept inside. There was a streetlamp shining through a big window that outlined many sacks of feed, standing open with their tops rolled down. One smelled of coconut meal. I grabbed a handful and stuffed it in my pants pocket. I put in another handful and then reached into another sack. It was rolled oats for breakfast cereal. I filled the other pocket with that and left, closing the door. But before I went out I put some of the oats with a dab of coconut meal in my mouth and started chewing it down. God, it was good! It seemed I was eating and tasting all the rich food smells of a stock feed store, the oaty alfalfa-like, heavy protein odors that make a man buying feed feel for the moment jealous of his ruminants. It was all there as I downed that mouthful and, slipping out, had another. Then, brushing from my lips the powdery sign of it, I eased back toward the gondola, but went first to the fountain in the station and drank, taking another mouthful of the mixture.

When I got to the gondola the fellows who had gotten out were getting back, so I did too. I stood looking down into the station, safe in the car, ready to travel, when I saw a heavy-set man rolling along in his walk in a familiar way. Then he was coming straight at me, looking up into my face—the Willits bull.

"Yeah, you stay where you are!" When he got to the boarding ladder, he climbed up on the coupling between the cars, keeping his eye on me and his gun in evidence on his hip. "Jump down on the other side," he growled. "I want to talk to you where we won't be bothered. Now," he snarled, "you double-crossing son of a bitch, where's the old geezer?" Then he spun from me, slamming into the steel side of the car with the back of his head and shoulders. He buckled, but the old man who'd spun him around slammed him against it again. He made an ineffectual reach for his weapon and the old man kicked his legs out from under him.

"Want another try for your courage there?" he asked as the bull, still fumbling for his gun, lifted a sick glance up at him and laid both hands out on the ballast in surrender.

"If I ever see you again," said the old man, "I'm gonna get sore. I 'us a sheriff for twelve years and know pret' near every top law enforcement officer in this land by his first name, and I've downed more killers than a man's got fingers, but I'll be damned if a fat, small town railroad bull like you don't try to hobble me. Look, bucko, my sons put out that reward and the charge won't stick."

"I got a family—" began the unstrung family man.

"I believe it," the old man cut in. "And you're pregnant again."

He jerked the bull to his feet, brushed him off, and headed him back up the tracks with a tremendous push. "Keep goin', Willie," he said, and in a gently benign tone: "Hustle yourself back to Willits and that paycheck will keep coming in ever' two weeks. Otherwise—well, I might get riled, and you figger your chances."

As we watched the bull hurrying up the tracks, sort of half looking around but never quite looking around, the locomotive hooted.

"Pile on," the old man said, and a self-satisfaction in his voice, muffled by the beard, made me relate it to the rich fodder smells of the feed store. After I was in, I helped him over the car's side and down into the gondola, noticing that for such acts he was stiff and halt as an old horse. In almost every way he was still a very formidable man, but age was slyly cutting that violent manhood to tatters about him, and I wondered if he knew it.

He caught me staring and brindled, guessing my conclusion. "Youth—aah," he started, eager to flay me with a tongue untamed by years, but stopped and forgot the desire. He leaned out over the side of the car and looked back up the tracks to where the bull had hurried off into the darkness. "We seen the last of that one anyway," he said in such a happy, friendly tone that I felt he thoroughly enjoyed his encounter.

We turned to other things. With his pocketknife, in lieu of the coin of the realm, he'd gotten two round marbles of gum from a gum machine in the station and now offered me one, but I'd already stuffed my mouth again with grain and that coconut cow feed added. I offered a handful to the old man.

"I just ain't that hungry, Clyde," he said. "Them oats ain't cooked, and raw starch like that's damn hard on a belly, especially one that's been without rations as long as yours has, and that coconut crud they feed to cows is nothing for a man's gut to conjure with. Spit it out and waller this gumball around for its sugar and easement."

But I didn't, and when I felt his eyes weren't cast my way in the darkness I gobbled down the rest of it—that is, all that didn't stick inside my pants pockets as a gummy paste. The food restored a certain sense of living, a feeling that I could do more than just endure. I looked back at the old man's set-to with the railroad bull and gloried in his dexterity and timing and in his certain knowledge of the man's reaction to his cool ferocity.

"How are you with a gun?" I asked as we moved around for warmth. "How are you with a six-shooter?" I thought he wasn't going to answer. We rocked along in the downpour between little hills I was sure were there, though in the darkness I couldn't see outside the gondola.

Finally he said that he was pretty good. "I was built for one," he said, staring down at the soft blur of his extended hands, "and I'll always wish I wasn't. If I'd felt that dexterity for a chisel or, say, a broadaxe or pen, I wouldn't be doing this traveling now."

"I'm afraid I don't get you," I said.

"Don't quite myself," he answered, more to himself than to me.

I shook myself, squirmed my back against my wet clothing and wrung out my hat. Nearing Marin County, I thought, nearing my friends—the hills of the Tiburon peninsula and the Bay. Tired as I was, an eagerness was in me. Partly because I was heading into the familiar—the land long emotionally felt, the old shoe feeling of horizons long known, the roads and groves of everyday experience. And then too, what I'd eaten was sending energy coursing through my blood. I felt much stronger, and thinking was no longer a chore.

"Look," I said to him, "I know every man follows some vision, though I'd be hard put to tell you why I had to go to the mountains, but I'm curious. Why do you travel?"

The fragrance of our engine's smoke blew down on us as he answered. "Some," he said, "has got to see it hellishin' plain afore they'll follow, and it has to blaze like a miracle for

131

others. But I got it," he went on, "that you and me follow standards we can only see from the corner of our eyes—not too often at that."

We passed a grade crossing where a few cars waited.

"You're right," I answered when we were again in darkness. "I've never seen one of my goals head on. But is it as vague as that with you? Don't that beard and the years it represents help you any?"

He swung around and peered at me in the darkness. "You're gettin' more chipper, Clyde," he said. "That uncooked cow feed's taken the limpness out of ya. No, the beard don't help that way. It just reminds me I got to hurry if I'm to find out."

"Find out?" I said, making it hang in the air between us with the question barely a query.

"An' it ain't quite as easy as that," he answered finally, "find out—that ain't exactly it. Guess I'm kind of ashamed to have such odd things for goals. They're more like courses. Well, what is it flows through a guy's life stronger than his long-term desires—freedom, knowledge, women, what's over the hill, and a guy's hankering to lose himself from the too familiar. At sixty I was fed up with the familiar, the same towns and the same country, the steps of the courthouse, the Rotary luncheons, and the damn lawyers. I never changed much, Clyde, except a certain part of my mind that grew and grew till it was ready to burst me in them surroundings. Hell, I told you I was a sheriff three terms—a fixture, like the horse trough in the square. I was the blue serge heaven their god-damn star was hung on. I sauntered among 'em doin' all the rigamarole a sheriff has to do these days: up on the bunting-covered stand and out on the farmland serving papers on honest, unfortunate people—shit and God's mercy, how I hated that part! And my sons grew up and swaggered off, eager to take up the same sad business of effecting justice."

"So you left to get away from the familiar," I said.

"Clyde," the old man replied after a denouncing silence, "you're smart enough to know that it's damn seldom a guy's moved by one reason. That was one part of it, sure, but there's other parts. I had to see if I was still man enough to live the life of those the law forced me to order out of town. I had to know I was at least equal to them in their hardships."

"Well," I said, "let's see if I can be as accurate about my goals."

"No, Clyde," he half beseeched me, "let me get on with this. I always figger along in here I can get it summed and really know why."

"You were talking about being equal to them in the rough go," I said.

"And still that weren't all of it," he went on. "It was the look they gave me when I set 'em free sometimes. The vags and the transients were the worst. They was over being sore. Maybe I'd been able to give 'em a break and they 'uz glad, but anyway they'd give me this look—a sort of 'you poor son of a bitch' look. I tell ya, I felt they pitied me, Clyde, for living the life of justice when liberty could be had if a guy weren't too mildewed under the trappings of safety. And they were right in a way with that look for there's stuff in this life that's—well, if I'd done this first I'd made a lot better sheriff."

"Why do you keep on?"

"It seems easier to share hardships than luxury. The world's made so some can loll while others grin and bear it, and I found I'm more content to be traveling with bums and with thinning soles and holes in my socks than mincing around with a Spode teacup and my ass on an embroidered cushion. Enough!" he said. "I ain't blabbed so much since I tried telling my oldest son about it three years ago." He deliberately turned from me, and I turned too and busied myself with restrapping my pack.

The tracks were running parallel to the highway and, on it going our way, a truck whose headlights picked out a long row of immense eucalyptus as it rushed along. The train picked up speed after we cut over a great flat by the bay. We could see the lights of Richmond and Berkeley, and the rain was faint on us and not so cold.

133

Then a sense of catastrophe gripped my middle, and light nausea, which interest in the old man's confession had hidden, grew overwhelming, making my *now* a canted, queazy unreality. I tried to reach the rail, but a cramp buckled me over and I butted into the corner of the car. I leaned over, jamming my head into that banging, vibrating steel corner and brought up all the stolen fodder. Then, when it was over, I went to the rail and hawked and spat until most of the vile green taste was gone.

The old man leaned beside me and stared out at the lights across the Bay. "The way you kept pawing that stuff in," he said, "I figgered it'd come to this—or else you'd start giving milk."

"They feed it to bulls too," I enunciated weakly. "Did you also expect me to sprout a ring in my nose?"

"Wouldn't need it," he replied. "The nearer you get home the more yours shows. You're just itching to have a lead chain snapped into yours for at least as long as you need to get over this trip." I grunted neither assent nor dissent. We pounded along and the air began to seem familiar and friendly. "You'd sell all the freedom there is right now," the old man said, "for a bowl of hot soup and your woman's smile."

"I'd be tempted."

"Don't blame you," he replied. "It's a flaw in your character, but I don't blame you."

The hills shut out the bay and the lights, and soon we slowed for San Rafael. After leaving San Rafael all us bums were on our feet and restless. Again the locomotive dragged the long line of banging, jerking boxcars, tank cars, and our gondola across a tideland flat, and the caboose followed like the rattles on the end of a diamondback's tail. The engine blew lustily, eagerly at crossings, seeming to exult in the long haul that it had made and anxious to get to the barn. Then faintly I could see the good loom of Mt. Tamalpais and we were slowing for the little tunnel at the beginning of the Tiburon peninsula. The engine's smoke was rank in there and then—bang, we were out, and the sky was lit up to the south. We rolled out on a trestle and the old familiar home road wound under it and the train was really slowing down. Around the edge of Belvedere's whale-like bulk the lights of San Francisco shone in the sky—a grail of a city beckoning to all who reached the shores of the bay. And though they didn't beckon to me, they reassured me: "All is well about the bay." I was staring hard, trying to get some faith from the lights—oh God, find them safe! Then the old man was beside me.

"Let me get this straight, Clyde," he mumbled. "You want me to come home with you and stay a bit and you say your Missus won't be sore?"

"We want you to spend the rest of the winter with us. I'm speaking for her too. Don't have a doubt. Why, we got grub enough, as I told you, so we'll have to throw some away if you don't stay, and duck hunting's swell out there and there's clam beds and I got a trotline."

"Okay," he said rather tensely. "It'll be good to take some ease, if it's plain like you say."

As we passed Hillarita the rain stopped and the long freight was easing into the yards of the terminal. As it slowed the noise of it slowed and it slowed even more and, well into the yards, it stopped. I had my pack by then and with the rest climbed out of the car and showed them how to get out of the yards. But I couldn't find Max or Glen. The old man said they'd gone on ahead over the cars as we were slowing and got off by the engine when she stopped, probably figuring to make the first car ferry across. We stumbled over stuff in the dark until we were clear of the yards. I told the old man of my friend, who lived half a mile out on the road home.

"He'll be glad to take us out in his old Buick," I said. "He stays up practically all night."

We trudged along. The sky was lightly overcast with still, thin clouds through which the moon bloomed, a vague radiance, and the bay air was balmy.

"No sleet in this country, eh?"

135

"Nope," I answered, "only a little hail once in a great while."

"Lemme try that pack, will ya? I never done much of that."

It sat too high on his shoulders, and the part that was supposed to rest on the back of his hips caught him high in the small of the back. We went on a bit farther and I saw that it irked him, being so poorly fit to him, so I took it back.

"I made it to fit just me," I said. "On me a lot of the weight isn't carried by the muscles of the torso but rests on the hips, and that saves energy."

"You're nearing home to babble happy like that, weary as you are."

"How about you?" I asked. "Aren't you worn pretty thin?"

"No," he said proudly, "I'm old and tough. That big feed I took on in Eureka was stashed onto a week's good living. I could go another day before I'd really feel it."

A silence followed, a silence in which we heard, far away, a boat whistle. We just put one slow foot in front of the other until we were climbing up the steps to Rodgers' place. Several cars were parked below it in the road, and when we got to the house we could see through the windows that the Rodgers were having a party. So I led the old man to the back porch, where he sat down in a wicker rocker.

"Go on in and visit and make your try for a lift."

"Yeah," I said, and slipped into the kitchen. From there I could see them dancing in the living room. They whirled by like the horses on a merry-go-round—and just as glassy-eyed, every last one, lit up to the eyebrows on Rodgers' bad booze.

Round and round they went, other men's wives in their arms and in their hands stemmed glasses slopping the bad booze that Rodgers made in the basement. Rodgers, looking through his own particular glaze, saw me and let out a bellow.

"Here's the kid back from gol' minin'!"

Their perfume and perspiration and whiskey breath came before them as they crowded into the kitchen around me. They slapped me on the back and offered me drinks. "Where's all the gol'?" they wanted to know. A rich, oily voice I didn't know and in back of me said, "Ya hit her rich, uh kid? Nice goin'!"

Then Mrs. Rodgers came out all loaded with satin and bracelets and her southern air. "Why, Clyde," she croaked and hiccuped, "ain't nobody given you a drink? Felix," she squalled, belching and excusing herself, "pour the boy a drink. He's probably had quite a tirin' day, hauling his ore and nuggets down from the mining country."

"Say when," Rodgers grunted, and started to pour.

"I can't handle it, Felix," I murmured, "but I got a friend on the porch who could use a double snort."

Rodgers poured it and, handing it to me, said, "I'll see you in a jiffy, pal."

I took the drink out to the old man and told him I'd see Rodgers in a minute for the lift home. As we spoke several of the women peered at us through the window of the back door, but when I went back to the kitchen it was empty. I needed something to eat badly and the icebox stood before me, but though I'd been on good terms with Rodgers for years, I found I couldn't help myself.

They were dancing again in the living room in the same manner as when I came in. Rodgers was dancing with little Mrs. Hahnstorp, and it seemed she was almost ardent—or just careless—the way she rubbed against him as they danced. And then I saw Mrs. Rodgers doing rather more as she swung by with Hahnstorp and, knowing their set fairly well, I knew how the night would end and that we hadn't a chance of getting a lift home.

A pie-eyed woman left the haunch-waggling women and the stealthy stalking that the men seemed to do with their feet and, leaning back, followed her pumps into the kitchen.

"Say, baby," she babbled, "I think you could use something more than refreshment." She opened the refrigerator, giving me a glimpse of stacks of fried chicken and a roast of beef. She picked up a shot glass from the table and poured that amount of tomato juice, then staggered over brightly and handed it to me. "There," she said, "you dirty miner type—that'll just fill you with vitamins, and I'll get you a sandwich from the tray." She dodged in amongst the dancers but didn't come back. I tossed the juice down and left.

"Not a chance," the old man said. "They won't stop shuffling until they flop. Let's get on out to your place."

We must've walked a mile before we first stopped. We leaned against a bank and rested, each deep in his own thoughts. Then we went on. The sky was clearing and the Bay lay down at the foot of the hills in a great luminous plain bordered on the far side by the lights of Berkeley and Oakland. Our road wound the convoluted hills, threading through this wooded glen and out upon that grassy promontory. Fear was in me that disaster had struck in some dread fashion while I was away. We walked a time in darkness under trees so thick that we knew each other only from the way our steps rattled the stones of the road, but out in the moonlight his beard shone and his nose jutted from the shadows of his Stetson as he slowly strode beside me.

"Here, lemme carry that pack," he said after another silent rest.

"But it don't fit you," I demurred.

He took it up and carried it on his shoulder for awhile and then put it on his back and trudged farther. After a mile, when we were resting, I took it and, fitting it to my back, slogged on silently.

I tried the word "Bunky" on my lips. He heard, so I didn't try "Nordi," but called it forth in mind: "Oh Nordi, be safe. God, make her safe!" And after awhile I was certain the old man knew how I felt, how he didn't exist anymore for me, but just those two in the little valley we headed toward, so I began to talk.

It was clattery talk and he didn't answer so I quit and just pushed on under my load and fears, and it seemed I could walk no farther. For awhile I was faint as I stumbled along, and then we began to near the ridge that hid the valley from our view, and again I built picket fences of weak, rattly talk—about the road mostly and about the lights across the bay and about the duck hunting we'd have. But as we neared the cove he must've felt we were close, for I could only speak in monosyllables. Were they there? Was there a home there any longer? Had an awful thing, a terrible accident, happened to one of them while I philandered with the mountains?

"Long walk you got from town."

"Yeah," I answered breathlessly. "It's just a little way farther."

For some reason that halted him in his stride, after which he made several stiff out-of-rhythm steps before he came on. I felt I would explode with panic in those moments before I could look down into the cove. I grabbed at possible deities, the runes of childhood. Oh, God, my heart pled, make them safe, hold them safe for me. I'll pay, God, anyway you like. And then the road passed through a clump of laurels and prickly leaf oaks. We were rounding the turn. Oh, God, God, step, step, we plodded along. I tried to say something to the old man but it stuck in my throat with a choked sound. Vaguely I knew that he broke stride again and fell behind me, and then the brink of the cove was below me and, as I trudged closer, I could look farther down, and then there it was.

It was small but burning bright down there, burning for me, a light in the window of home. I stood there torn with a strange anguish, sobbing with relief, but controlled myself before he got to me. We both stood looking down, and after a time he said: "It's all right now, ain't it, son?"

I didn't dare to talk. "Uh, huh," I said.

But by the time we came to the gate and I slid back the familiar oaken bolt, I was talking and eager again.

"Wait'll you see her. You and her'll take to each other like long lost pals. And the kid's not snotty or smarty. He's real good company already."

The old man didn't reply.

"Over there on that flat's the garden," I went on, "and the spring's right above us here. It's piped to tanks and then down to the garden."

"Good idea," he said from behind me.

I wanted to slow so we could walk abreast, but I couldn't —the lighted window and walking down hill—I couldn't slow for him.

"She'll have coffee made in a jiffy," I said over my shoulder. "Your room's just to the left of that light."

Then all of a sudden I couldn't talk anymore, for I was remembering Nordi's smile when I first met her. I called then: "Nordi, Nordi, Bunky!" It wasn't loud, I couldn't call loud, but hurried on a dozen steps calling again and again, and I took fright: something had happened!

In anguish I called again: "Nordi, it's me," and the door opened.

I stopped frozen where I stood not far from the door.

"Clyde?" she called, raising the lamp she carried, "Clyde?" And then, seeing me struck still in the vague perimeter of the lamplight: "Oh, Clyde, dear, you're here! Bunky said you'd be. We stayed up and waited, he was so sure."

She came out farther from the door holding the lamp higher: "Come in, Clyde—drop that awful pack on the porch and come into us."

"Sure," I said lamely.

It was then that I remembered the old man. I looked around and couldn't see him.

"Hold the lamp higher, Nordi. I brought a friend."

"Listen," she whispered, and we both heard him smash through some bushes up the hill from us. Then we could hear his feet on the stones of the road. I tried to remember his name; I didn't know his name!

"Hey!" I halloed. "Come back. She's waiting for us."

Then the moon came out real bright and I flung my pack down and started up after him, but he must have seen me, for the noise of his flight stopped.

"Go back, Clyde," he called to me, and the resonance of it came down the hill, "go back. It's not for me, boy."

We both waited in the silence for a long time. I looked down where, below me by the house, Nordi held the light.

"Are you sure?" I bellowed finally, wondering how he felt at the moment.

"I'm sure," he answered from above and far away. "Sure as I'm sure of anything."

"Not even for the night and a couple of hot meals?" I cried, louder across the distance, and he answered me from still farther away, and faintly I could still hear his shoes on the stones of the road. He answered, but not at all loudly, and I couldn't make out what he said, and stood sad and without thought for awhile, but finally I turned and headed down to where she stood holding the lamp.